Never
Give Up!

Holt
Basic
Reading

Never Give Up!

Bernard J. Weiss
Reading and Linguistics

Eldonna L. Evertts
Language Arts

Loreli Steuer
Reading and Linguistics

Janet Sprout
Educational Consultant

Lyman C. Hunt
General Editor — Satellite Books

Level 11

HOLT, RINEHART AND WINSTON, PUBLISHERS
New York • Toronto • London • Sydney

ISBN: 0-03-047836-7
90123   071   987654321

Acknowledgments:

Grateful acknowledgment is given to the following authors and publishers.

American Heritage Press and Jonathan Cape, Ltd., for "Alexander and the Magic Mouse," adapted from *Alexander and the Magic Mouse* by Martha Sanders and illustrated by Philippe Fix. Text copyright © 1969 by Martha Sanders. Illustrations copyright © 1969 by American Heritage Press. Used by permission.

Brandt & Brandt, for "After the Party," from *Jonathan Blake* by William Wise. Copyright © 1956 by William Wise. Used by permission.

Coward, McCann & Geoghegan, Inc., and Russell & Volkening, Inc., for "George Washington's Breakfast," freely adapted from *George Washington's Breakfast* by Jean Fritz. Copyright © 1969 by Jean Fritz. Used by permission.

E. P. Dutton & Co., Inc., for "The Hole in the Tree," from the book *The Hole in the Tree,* written and illustrated by Jean Craighead George. Copyright © 1957 by Jean Craighead George. Used by permission.

E. P. Dutton & Co., Inc., and The Bodley Head Ltd., for "Do You Have the Time, Lydia?" Adapted from *Do You Have the Time, Lydia?* by Evaline Ness. Text and illustrations copyright © 1971 by Evaline Ness. Used by permission.

Follett Publishing Company and Brockhampton Press Limited, for "Gumdrop on the Move," adapted from *Gumdrop on the Move* by Val Biro. Copyright © 1969 by Val Biro. Used by permission.

Follett Publishing Company, for "Five Hundred Thousand Miles," from *That Was Summer* by Marci Ridlon. Copyright © 1969 by Marci Ridlon. For "Walking in the Fog," from *Farther Than Far* by Margaret Hillert. Copyright © 1969 by Margaret Hillert. Used by permission.

Golden Gate Junior Books, Division of Children's Press, for an adaptation from *The Once-A-Year Day* by Eve Bunting, illustrated by W. T. Mars. Used by permission.

Harcourt Brace Jovanovich, Inc., Lemniscaat Rotterdam, English translation by Oxford University Press, for "The Golden Treasure," adapted from *The Golden Treasure* by Maryke Reesink. Copyright © 1968 by Lemniscaat Rotterdam and Oxford University Press. Used by permission.

Harper & Row, Publishers, Inc., for "The Spangled Pandemonium," from *Beyond the Pawpaw Trees* by Palmer Brown. Copyright © 1954 by Palmer Brown. For "Old Log House," from *A World to Know* by James S. Tippett. Copyright 1933 by Harper & Brothers, renewed © 1961 by Martha K. Tippett. For "Flat Stanley," adapted from *Flat Stanley* by Jeff Brown. Copyright © 1964 by Jeff Brown. Used by permission.

Harper & Row, Publishers, Inc., and Methuen & Co. Ltd., for "Little House in the Big Woods," excerpted from *Little House in the Big Woods* by Laura Ingalls Wilder. Copyright 1932 by Laura Ingalls Wilder, renewed © 1960 by Rose Wilder Lane. Used by permission.

Hawthorn Books, Inc., for "The Talking Leaves," adapted from *The Story of Sequoyah* by Bernice Kohn. Copyright © 1969 by Bernice Kohn. Used by permission.

Holt, Rinehart and Winston, Publishers, for "Tikki Tikki Tembo," adapted from the Holt, Rinehart edition of *Tikki Tikki Tembo* retold by Arlene Mosel. Copyright © 1968 by Arlene Mosel. Used by permission.

Holt, Rinehart and Winston, Publishers, and Curtis Brown Ltd., for "My Name," from *Kim's Place and Other Poems* by Lee Bennett Hopkins. Copyright © 1974 by Lee Bennett Hopkins. Used by permission.

Little, Brown and Company and Curtis Brown, Ltd., for "Joe," from *Far and Few* by David McCord. Copyright 1952 by David McCord. Used by permission.

Lothrop, Lee & Shepard Co., for "Fidelia," adapted from *Fidelia* by Ruth Adams. Copyright © 1970 by Ruth Adams. For "A Single Flower," from *Hello, Small Sparrow* by Hannah Lyons Johnson. Published 1971 by Lothrop, Lee & Shepard Co. Used by permission.

Art Credits:

Photo Credits:

Table of Contents

UNIT FOUR
OTHER PLACES

SMALL DISCOVERIES

Walking in the Fog

Out in the fog, out in the fog
All gray and misty white,
I hear some muffled scraps of sound,
But no one is in sight.

Only a voice, only a step.
I strain my eyes to see.
Then suddenly, suddenly from the fog
My friend steps out at me.

—*Margaret Hillert*

Flat Stanley

Story by Jeff Brown
Illustrated by Tomi Ungerer

PART ONE
Flat as a Pancake

"Breakfast is ready," said Mrs. Lambchop to Mr. Lambchop. "I'll get the boys up."

Just then their younger son, Arthur, yelled from the bedroom, "Come and look!"

Mr. and Mrs. Lambchop went into the boys' bedroom. "Look at Stanley's bed," said Arthur.

Across the bed lay a large bulletin board on which the boys pinned up pictures and things. It fell on Stanley in the night.

Stanley wasn't hurt. "What's going on here?" he called out from under the bulletin board.

Mr. Lambchop hurried to pick up the bulletin board. "Oh," he said. "Stanley's flat!"

"As a pancake," said Mrs. Lambchop. "Queerest thing I've ever seen. Let's have breakfast, and then Stanley and I will go see Doctor Dan."

"How do you feel, Stanley?" Doctor Dan asked. "Does it hurt very much?"

"I felt kind of funny for a while after I got up," Stanley said. "But I feel fine now."

"Well, that's how it is with these cases," said Doctor Dan. "We'll just have to keep an eye on this young man."

When Stanley got used to being flat, he liked it. He could go in and out of a room, even when the door was closed, just by going under the door.

Arthur tried to go under a door, but he hurt his head.

One day Stanley was walking with his mother when her ring fell off. It rolled down through the bars that covered a dark, deep hole in the sidewalk. Mrs. Lambchop began to cry.

"I have an idea," Stanley said. He took the laces out of his shoes and tied them together. Then he tied one end of the laces to his belt and gave the other end to his mother.

"Let me down slowly," he said, "and I'll look for your ring."

Mrs. Lambchop let Stanley down through the bars. He looked all over for the ring. At last he found it, and Mrs. Lambchop pulled him up.

"Thank you, Stanley," she said. "Having you flat is very handy."

One day Stanley got a letter from a friend who had moved to California. School was over, and Stanley's friend asked him to come to California for a visit.

"Oh, boy!" Stanley said. "I'd love to go!"

Mr. Lambchop said, "I can't afford to send you all the way to California by airplane. I'll have to think of some other way."

When Mr. Lambchop came home that night, he had a large brown-paper envelope. "Now then, Stanley," he said, "see if this will fit. Then we can afford to send you to California."

The envelope fit Stanley very well. There was even room left over for a sandwich.

The next day Mr. and Mrs. Lambchop slid Stanley into his envelope, along with the sandwich. They mailed him from the box on the corner.

Mrs. Lampchop was worried because Stanley had never been away from home alone before. She knocked on the box. "Can you hear me, dear?" she called. "Are you all right?"

"I'm fine," Stanley said in a loud voice.

Then Mr. and Mrs. Lambchop said good-by and went home.

Stanley had a fine time in California. When the visit was over, Stanley's friend returned him in a beautiful, large white envelope.

Back home Stanley told his family that he had had a wonderful trip.

On Sunday afternoons Mr. Lambchop always liked to take the boys off with him to a museum or to the park. But it was hard to hold on to two boys who were never still. It was easier after Stanley got flat. Mr. Lambchop rolled Stanley up and tied some string around him. Then he could carry Stanley by the string and hold on to Arthur with the other hand.

Stanley didn't mind being carried because he had never liked to walk. Arthur didn't like to walk but he had to, and it made him jealous of Stanley.

One Sunday afternoon the Lambchops met an old friend of Mr. Lambchop's. "Well, George, I see you have bought some wallpaper," the man said.

"Wallpaper?" said Mr. Lambchop. "Oh, no. This is my son Stanley." He untied the string and unrolled Stanley.

"How do you do?" Stanley said.

"Nice to meet you," the man said. Then he said to Mr. Lambchop,

"George, that boy is flat."

"Bright, too," said Mr. Lambchop. "Stanley does very well in school."

That night Mr. and Mrs. Lambchop heard a noise in the living room. They found Arthur on the floor with a great many large books on top of him.

"Put some more on me," Arthur said when he saw them. "Don't just stand there. Help me."

Mr. and Mrs. Lambchop sent him back to bed, and the next morning they had a talk with Stanley. "Arthur can't help being jealous of you because you're flat," they said. "Be nice to him. You're his big brother."

One day Stanley and Arthur were in the park. Many other boys were flying beautiful kites.

"Someday," Arthur said, "I'll have a big kite, and I'll win a kite-flying contest, and everyone will know me. **No one** knows me these days."

Stanley remembered what his mother and dad had said about Arthur's being jealous. He went to a boy with a broken kite and asked if he could use his string.

"You can fly me, Arthur," he said. "Come on." Stanley tied the string to himself and gave Arthur the string to hold. He ran across the grass. Then he turned to meet the breeze.

Up, up, up went Stanley, being a kite. He knew just how to fly on the wind. He went right into it if he wanted to go higher. And he let the wind take him from behind to go faster.

Stanley was a beautiful sight, green and brown in the blue sky. Everyone in the park stood still to watch. No one ever flew the way Stanley Lambchop flew that day. Maybe no one ever will again.

After a while, of course, people grew tired of watching, and Arthur grew tired of running about.

Three boys asked Arthur to go with them for a hot dog. Arthur left the string stuck in a tree. He didn't notice that the string was getting all caught up in the tree. Stanley got stuck in the branches. Twenty minutes went by before Arthur heard him yelling and set him free.

Stanley would not talk to Arthur that night. He said he was sorry, but Stanley was mad.

Two Good Ideas

Mr. and Mrs. O. Jay Dart lived in the apartment above the Lambchops. Mr. Dart was in charge of the Museum of Art. At breakfast one morning, Stanley heard his father talking about Mr. Dart.

"I see," said Mr. Lambchop, reading the paper, "that still another great painting has been stolen from the museum. It says that Mr. O. Jay Dart is at his wits' end. The police and the guards can't seem to find the thieves."

Early the next morning Stanley heard Mr. Dart talking to his wife in the elevator. "These sneak thieves work at night," Mr. Dart said. "It's very hard for our guards to stay awake when they have been working all day."

That gave Stanley an idea. He told Mr. Dart all about it.

"Stanley," Mr. Dart said, "if your mother will let you, I will put you and your plan to work tonight!"

Mrs. Lambchop said Stanley could carry out his plan if he would rest all afternoon. "I won't have you up that late without some rest."

Early that night Stanley went with Mr. Dart to a big hall in the museum. Mr. Dart showed Stanley a very large painting. "That," he said, "is one of the greatest paintings in the world!"

Then Mr. Dart took Stanley to another room and said, "It's time for you to get ready." He took out a pretty white dress, some little shoes, a wide straw hat, a wig, and a stick.

"If you wear these," Mr. Dart said, "you'll look like a painting that belongs in the big hall."

Stanley was very upset when he saw the dress. "I'll look like a girl," he said. "I wish I had never had my idea." But he had promised to help, so he put on the dress.

Back in the big hall, Mr. Dart helped Stanley climb up into a picture frame across from the great painting. In the beautiful frame, Stanley looked just like a picture of a sheep girl.

Mr. Dart went off, and Stanley was alone in the big dark hall. Time went by and Stanley got tired. Anyone would get tired of standing in a picture frame. "Maybe the thieves won't come," Stanley thought.

The moon went behind a cloud, and then the big hall was really dark. Stanley heard a sound.

Creeeeeeeeek....

The strange sound came again. Then Stanley saw a light. A trap door had opened in the floor, and two men came up into the hall!

"This is it," said one of the thieves. "This is where we pull one of our biggest jobs while everyone sleeps."

"Right," said the other man. "In all this great city there is no one to see us."

The thieves took the great painting off the wall. Then one of the thieves looked over at Stanley.

"Look at the strange sheep girl in this painting," he said. "I thought sheep girls always smiled. This one looks scared."

Just in time, Stanley smiled.

"She looks happy to me," said the other man. "And what a pretty little thing she is, too."

Pretty! That really made Stanley mad. He waited until the sneak thieves had turned back to the other painting, and then he yelled in a loud, scary voice,

"POLICE! POLICE! MR. DART! THE SNEAK THIEVES ARE HERE!"

"I think I heard the sheep girl yelling," said one of the thieves quietly. "Oh, boy! Yelling pictures! We need a rest."

"You'll get a rest, all right!" yelled Mr. Dart, running in with the police and guards. Before they knew it, the thieves were led away to jail.

The next morning Stanley Lambchop had his picture in the newspaper.

For a while everywhere Stanley went people looked at him. He could hear them whisper, "Look at that boy over there. That's Stanley Lambchop. He's the one who caught the sneak thieves."

And then something strange began to happen. People didn't whisper anymore. They laughed and made fun of Stanley as he went by. They yelled mean things about the way he looked.

Stanley told his father how he felt. "It's the other children I mind most," he said. "They don't like me anymore because I'm different."

"It's not right to make fun of people because they're different," Mr. Lambchop said.

"I know," Stanley said. "Only maybe it's hard for everyone to like everyone."

That night Arthur heard Stanley crying. He went over to his bed. "Are you okay?" he asked.

"Go away," Stanley said.

"Please let's be friends." Arthur couldn't help crying a little, too. "Oh, Stanley," he said. "Please tell me what's the matter."

"The thing is," Stanley said, "I'm tired of being flat. I want to be like other people again."

Arthur could think of nothing to say. So he took hold of Stanley's hand. The two brothers sat together in the dark, being friends. They were still sad, but each one felt a little better than before.

Then Arthur jumped up, turned on the light, and ran to a big box where toys were kept.

"Here it is," Arthur said. He had found what he wanted, an old pump. The boys looked at each other.

"Okay," Stanley said at last. "But take it easy." He put one end of the pump in his mouth.

"I'll go slowly," Arthur said. "If it hurts, wave your hand at me."

Arthur began to pump. At first nothing happened, but soon Stanley's face got a little round. Arthur watched Stanley's hand, but there was no wave, so he pumped on. Slowly Stanley began to get round.

**"It's working!
It's working!"**
yelled Arthur.

Stanley got bigger and bigger. The buttons on the top of his pajamas popped off. A minute more and Stanley was round again. Arthur stopped pumping. There stood Stanley as he used to be, as if he had never been flat at all!

"Thank you very much, Arthur," Stanley said.

The brothers were shaking hands when Mr. Lambchop came into the room with Mrs. Lambchop right behind him. "We heard you up and talking when you should be asleep!" said Mrs. Lambchop.

"George!" said Mrs. Lambchop.
"Stanley's round!"

"I'm the one who did it," Arthur said.

Everyone was very happy, of course. And all the family told Arthur how wonderful he was.

Then Mr. and Mrs. Lambchop put the boys back into their beds and gave them each a good-night kiss.

Never Make Fun

Never make fun of a turtle, my son,
   For moving so slow in a race.
He *prefers* to move slow and he thinks that *you* go
   At a terrible, nerve-wracking pace.

Don't ever sneer at a beaver, my dear,
   Because of the size of his tooth.
He wonders why all of your teeth are so small,
   And thinks that *your* grin is uncouth.

It's vulgar to laugh at a baby giraffe.
   His neck is unusual, that's true.
But I tell you he's glad to resemble his dad,
  And would hate
   To be shaped
   Like you!

—*Martin Gardner*

Evaline Ness

Do You Have The Time, Lydia?

Once there was a girl named Lydia. She lived with her father, who grew plants. And she lived with her brother, Andy. Their house was near a warm sea.

Every day Lydia was busy painting pictures and reading books. She was busy gathering shells and making clothes for the cat. Lydia was so busy with so many things, she never finished any of them.

Her brother Andy didn't do anything. He didn't know how to do anything. Some days, he asked Lydia to help him do things. All the time, she said, *"No, no, no, no! I haven't got time!"*

One day her father heard Lydia say, *"No, no, no, no! I haven't got time!"* Her father said, "Oh ho! If you take time, you can have time."

But Lydia was too busy to listen.

One bright morning, Andy walked down to the beach. He found an old lobster trap. He pulled it home and into Lydia's room. She sat making a dress for the cat.

"Look!" he yelled. "A race car! Please, oh please, Lydia, fix it for me. I want to be in Dr. Arnold's race! The boy or girl who wins gets a dog!"

Without looking up, Lydia said, "No, no, no, no! I haven't got time!"

"The race is this afternoon!" cried Andy. Lydia stopped her work long enough to look at the trap.

"Well, all right. I'll fix it. But later."

"You don't care!" cried Andy.

"I said I'd fix it, didn't I?"

Andy looked at Lydia for a long time. Then, slowly, he backed out of the room.

Lydia dropped the cat's dress. She found her roller skates. Lydia pulled the front wheels from the back wheels. She tied each set of wheels to one of the four corners of the trap. Then she cut two large paper lights for the front of the car. She took her doll's box and dumped everything in it onto the floor. She then placed the box in the trap for a place to sit.

"Fine!" said Lydia. "All it needs is a steering wheel. And I know just where to find one!"

Lydia ran to her father's old greenhouse. In one corner was some junk. At the very top was an old wheel. As Lydia reached for the wheel she saw a large glass bowl.

"All that needs," said Lydia, "is some water and a few fish. And I know just where to find them!"

Away Lydia raced. She went through the pine trees and down to the boathouse. She wanted to get her fishing net.

The first thing she saw there was her father's rowboat filled with water. Lydia tried to tip the boat over. It would not move. She found an old can in the boathouse. Lydia started to take out the water. But the more she took out, the more water came in. Lydia threw the can down. She ran up the beach to the greenhouse to tell her father.

Halfway there, Lydia stopped. On the beach lay a bird that was hurt. Its eyes were closed and one wing was broken. Just as Lydia started to pick it up, the bird opened its eyes. The bird slapped Lydia's face with its good wing.

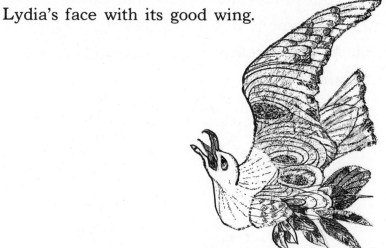

"You need a doctor!" yelled Lydia. "And I know just where to find one!"

She began to run. She ran fast. By the time she reached Dr. Arnold's house, she was out of breath. But Dr. Arnold was not home. Stuck to the door was a note. It said: Back in 10 Minutes. At Race.

The race!

Up the street flew Lydia. At the top of the hill she came to a quick stop. There stood Andy, alone. The race was over. All the cars were at the foot of the hill. Dr. Arnold was just giving a dog to the boy who won.

Andy looked at Lydia. There were big tears in his eyes. Then he turned and ran.

"Andy!" cried Lydia. "I was fixing it, but I didn't have enough time!"

Andy kept running. He didn't look back.

Lydia watched him until he turned a corner. Then she walked back to Dr. Arnold's house. She sat down on the doorstep and cried and cried. Then she stopped because she had no tears left.

Suddenly a voice said, "Well! Have you finished your crying?"

Lydia looked down and saw Dr. Arnold's shoes. Then she looked up and saw Dr. Arnold's face. Lydia said, "I guess at last I took time to finish something."

Dr. Arnold looked at Lydia. "Now what?" he asked.

Then Lydia remembered the hurt bird.

"The bird!" she yelled. "Dr. Arnold! It's hurt. It's on the beach. It can't fly!"

"Hurry," she cried. Dr. Arnold went into his house to get his black bag.

"Hurry!" she called as she ran to the beach.

At last they were there, and there was the bird. Dr. Arnold took the bird and fixed its bad wing.

"This bird will be just fine," said Dr. Arnold. "But it can't fly right now. Why don't you take the bird home, Lydia? Feed it a nice fat fish when it wakes up. That is, if you have the time."

Lydia looked down at the sleeping bird.

"Oh ho! I'll take time!" said Lydia.

After Dr. Arnold left, Lydia took the bird home. She put grass in the bottom of a box. Then with care, she placed the bird on its cool bed.

Lydia went to look for Andy. She found him in the backyard. Lydia placed the bird in its box in front of Andy.

"Andy," said Lydia. "Look what I found for you. It will be real when it wakes up. You can have it all for your own."

Andy looked at the bird. He said nothing.

"Did you know that dogs can't fly?" asked Lydia.

Not looking at Lydia, Andy said, "I don't want your old bird."

Lydia left the bird with Andy and went back to the old greenhouse. She found the wheel. As she left, Lydia saw a birdhouse. She had started to make it a long time ago. All it needed was a roof.

"What that birdhouse needs . . ." began Lydia. She stopped. She looked at the wheel in her hand. ". . . is nothing!"

Lydia shot out of the old greenhouse. She ran into the house to her room.

She finished putting the wheel in place. Then a voice at her back said, "I don't want your old trap."

"Oh, Andy!" cried Lydia. "Yes you do, too! I'll give you my whistle. The trap will be a fire truck."

It was quiet for a long time.

"Will it have a ladder?" asked Andy.

"A ladder too! I promise! I promise!"

"But you don't have the time," said Andy.

"Oh no? Oh ho! If I take time, I can have time!" said Lydia.

FIXING THINGS

These people all help us in a special way. They fix our broken furniture, TV sets, cars, and locks. Can you tell which job each person does?

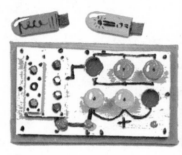

What can you do when your TV stops working? You can ask this woman to help you. She will check the tubes and wires in your set to find out what the trouble is.

When something is wrong with your car, this man can help. He is an auto mechanic. To do his job, he had to learn all about cars and how cars are built. As you can see, he has to be able to work with his hands.

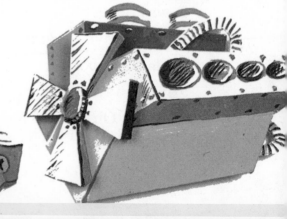

Has the arm of your favorite chair ever been broken? Has your family ever wanted to change the color of your dining room table? This woman can handle both jobs. She repairs and refinishes furniture. Here she is polishing the frame of a chair with a soft cloth. Next she will fix the seat and back of the chair.

If you ever lost the keys to your house, this man probably helped you. He is a locksmith. He uses special tools to open the door. He can also make new keys and fix or replace broken locks.

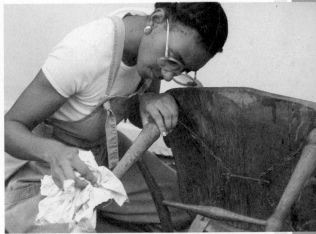

Do you like to work with your hands? Then maybe you'd like to do one of these jobs when you are older.

Jean Craighead George

The Hole in the Tree

The apple tree in the farmyard was growing old. Its bottom branches reached down to the earth. When the leaves covered the branches, there was a secret room under the tree.

Scott and Paula Gordon liked the secret room.

One summer morning, Scott was in the room, digging a hole for a box. A beetle flew by. She landed on his arm. Scott brushed the beetle off his arm and onto the tree. The beetle folded her wings and started climbing the tree.

Scott dug deeper into the earth. He did not notice the beetle bite into the tree. This small bite was the beginning of the hole in the tree. The beetle went on biting into the tree. Soon the beetle had made a tunnel. She laid her eggs in the tunnel.

Later, Old Stonehead, a woodpecker, found the small beetle hole. He started pecking. He pecked the wood very fast. Scott and Paula watched. It seemed to them his head would fly off. He made the hole bigger.

The hole was now as big as a housefly. It still seemed small. But to something not much bigger than a housefly, such a hole could be a home.

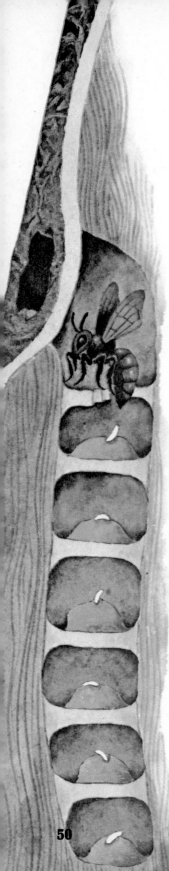

A large carpenter bee came to the hole in the tree. It was just what she wanted. But it was too small. She began to bite the hole bigger and bigger. At day's end, the hole was as big as Paula's thumb. Inside the tree, the carpenter bee had made a tunnel. The tunnel went down. It was almost as long as Paula's foot. At the bottom of the tunnel, the carpenter bee placed some good things to eat. Then she laid her eggs.

The baby bees were born in the fall. Winter came, and the bees stayed inside the tree. In the spring they came out again. Most of the bees flew out of the hole to find new homes. But one little bee stayed. It wanted to make its home in the apple tree. But a hole in a tree is not an easy thing to keep. The bee was out eating one day. Then a chickadee found the bee-hole. It was too small, but she pecked away. She dug and pecked and dug and pecked. By night the hole in the tree was bigger. It was as big as a wristwatch. The chickadee worked for seven more days. She made the hole seven hands deeper. She then made a nest at the bottom of the hole. Into the nest she put some rabbit fur.

Two days later she laid a small egg. Every morning she laid another egg until there were seven. Twelve days later there were seven little chickadees.

Paula and Scott came to the secret room. They heard a sound coming from the tree. They looked in. "A chickadee nest," cried Scott. Paula and Scott watched the chickadee feed her young.

One day a baby chickadee sat in the doorway of the hole. She was pushed from behind. She flew to a nearby branch. In the doorway sat another little chickadee. He was pushed from behind and flew to the branch. In this way seven little chickadees came out of the hole. Paula and Scott watched them fly into the treetops all summer.

In the fall a field mouse came to live in the tree. She made the chickadee nest over into a mouse nest. Soon five baby mice came out of the tree. Paula and Scott left food for the mice. But the mice never found it. They had already left.

Old Stonehead, the woodpecker, had returned. He had scared the mice out of the nest. After making the hole bigger, Stonehead lived in it all winter. But soon it was spring. Many birds and animals wanted the hole. The flying squirrels took it from Stonehead. He had stayed out late one night. The bluebirds pecked until they got it from the flying squirrels. Many other birds came. They had fights over the hole. Each one made it bigger. It was now as big as a baseball and very deep.

When summer came, the hole had a new owner. It wasn't a bird. It wasn't an animal. It was Scott. He found that the hole was now large enough to hold many of his things. He put a quarter and a ball of string into the hole.

But then a queen carpenter ant found the hole. She laid many eggs. The eggs became worker ants. They made many more tunnels in the tree. The queen laid more eggs. Then there were more workers. And more tunnels. And more eggs. Soon there was an army of ants.

When Scott came back to get his things, the ants bit him. Scott sat down to plan a war on the army of ants. But the war never came about.

Old Stonehead had come back! He pecked again at the hole. He cleaned out the ants. The woodpecker made the hole as big as Scott's head.

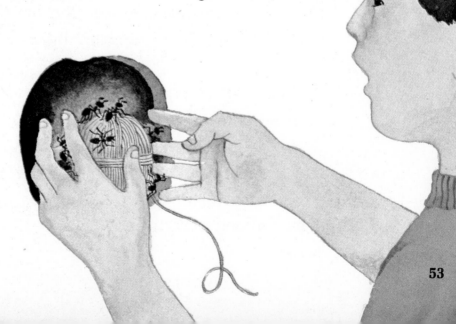

Paula took this bigger hole for her own. Into it she put a cup, a baseball, and a broken doll. She put in a note for Scott, too. It read, "There's going to be a new baby at our house. I hope it's a girl. Paula." Winter came to the land. Paula forgot the things in the tree.

In the dark of night, someone went into the hole. She put the cup on her head. She put her arms around the doll. Then Fumbles, the raccoon, fell asleep.

Fumbles got up one day to find it snowing. She didn't like snow. So she went back into the hole. She was fat and did not need to eat all winter. She had the driest hole on the farm. It had white walls and lovely toys. Fumbles closed her eyes and began her long winter sleep.

Winter went and spring came. Another raccoon came into the hole. It was Mask, the mate of Fumbles. He put the cup on his foot. Fumbles got up. She saw her mate. And she went back to sleep.

One day, Scott came to the hole to hide an old trap. He saw some fur coming out of the hole.

"Fur," he cried. "Who's put a fur hat in my hole?" He ran and told Paula. She said they should write a note for whoever left the hat.

"Be careful," it read. They placed it on the fur hat. The next day the note was gone. But the hat wasn't.

"If we can't scare him, we'll make friends," said Paula. She wrote another note.

"Who are you? Let's be friends," it read.

The next day that note was gone. The hat was still there. Scott and Paula sat down to talk over another plan.

"We'll just have to take the hat into the house," said Scott. "The owner will have to knock at the door to get it." Just then, Fumbles looked out of the hole.

"Of course," Paula answered and stood up to get the hat. Boy and girl and raccoon looked at one another. All were surprised.

Fumbles went back into the hole. As she did, she dropped a bit of paper. Scott picked it up and read it. It said, "There's . . . baby . . . house . . . Pa . . . ."

Scott put his ear to the tree. Through the walls of the tree came the sounds of baby raccoons. He heard Fumbles and her mate, too.

"Isn't that something," said Scott.

"It sure is," said Paula.

From the house, Mr. Gordon called, "Paula! Scott! You have a baby sister!"

A beetle landed on Scott's arm. He brushed her off. He and Paula left the secret room. They ran to the house. The beetle did not see them running happily into the house.

The beetle was climbing the tree. She was looking for a good place to bite a hole in the tree.

Mexicali Soup

Kathryn Hitte and William D. Hayes

All the way across town Mama sang to herself. There on the street of the great fine city, she sang a song from the old home in the mountains. And she thought of what she would get in the little stores.

Only the best of everything! Potatoes and peppers—the best! Tomatoes and beans—the best! The best garlic and corn! And then, cooked all together, ah! Mama's special Mexicali Soup. The soup that always made everyone say, "Mama makes the best soup in the world."

"Ah," Mama thought, "dinner tonight will be very special for my Rosa and Pablo and Juan and Manuel and Maria, and for my little one, and for Papa, too."

"Mama, Mama! Wait a minute," called Maria, running out of school with her new city friend. "May I play awhile with Ann? Please?"

"Very well," Mama said. "Awhile. But do not be late for dinner, Maria. I am making my special soup tonight."

"Mmm-mmm, Mexicali Soup!" Maria said. Then she looked thoughtful. "But, Mama?"

"Yes, Maria?" Mama said.

"Mama, there are such a lot of potatoes in your Mexicali Soup."

"Of course," Mama said, smiling.

"Ann doesn't eat potatoes. Her mother doesn't eat them. Her sister doesn't eat them. Potatoes make you fat, Mama," said Maria. "I think we should do what others do here. We are no longer in the mountains of the West, Mama, where everyone eats potatoes. We are in the city now. So would you—Mama, would you please

leave out the potatoes?"

"No potatoes," Mama said. She looked at Maria. Her face was thoughtful. "Well, there are plenty of good things in the Mexicali Soup without potatoes. I will put in more of everything else. It will still make good soup."

"Of course, it will," Maria said, hugging Mama. "You make the best soup in the world."

Mama went on to the street of the little stores, thinking as she went.
"Tomatoes,
beans,
corn,
green peppers,
red peppers, good and hot,
and garlic,
but *no potatoes!*"

Mama went to one little store for the best tomatoes and corn. She went to another for the best beans and garlic. "And the peppers," she thought to herself. "I will get the peppers from Pablo, our own Pablo, at the store where he works."

Pablo came hurrying out of the store to the little stand on the sidewalk.

"Let me help you, Mama! I hope you want something very good for our dinner tonight. I get very hungry working here," Pablo said.

"Yes, Pablo," Mama said. "For tonight— something special!" She reached for the hot red peppers. "Mexicali Soup!"

"That's great," Pablo said. Then he looked thoughtful. "But, Mama—"

"Yes?" Mama said, putting some peppers in a bag.

"Well—Mama, you use a lot of hot peppers in your soup," said Pablo.

"Of course," Mama said, smiling.

"A lot," Pablo said again. "People here don't do that. They don't cook or eat the way we did in the mountains of the West."

"I know, Mama. I have worked here for weeks now, after school and Saturdays. And in all that time, Mama, I have not sold as many hot peppers to other women as you use in a week. Please *don't put hot peppers in the soup,* Mama," Pablo said.

"No peppers," Mama said. She looked at Pablo. His face was thoughtful. "Well—there are plenty of good things in the soup without peppers. I will put in more of something else. It will still make good soup."

Pablo put the peppers back on the stand. "Of course, it will, Mama." He kissed her. "Everyone knows you make the best soup in the world."

Mama went on home. "Tomatoes, beans, garlic, corn," she said to herself. "Yes, I can still make a good soup with those."

She sang to herself as she walked across the street.

"Mama!" Juan and Manuel called. They left their game of stickball and ran over to Mama.

"Oh, boy! Groceries!" said Juan when he saw the bags. He opened one of them. "Tomatoes and corn—I know what we're having for dinner."

"Me, too," said Manuel. He looked into the other bag. "Beans and garlic. Mexicali Soup! Right, Mama?" Manuel smiled. Then he looked thoughtful. "But, Mama — listen."

"I am listening," Mama said.

"Well, I think we use an awful lot of beans," Manuel said. "They don't use so many beans in the school lunch. You know, Mama, they have different ways of doing things here. They are different from the ways of our town on the side of the mountain. I think we should try new ways. I think we shouldn't use so many beans. Mama, please make Mexicali Soup *without beans.*"

"Manuel is right!" Juan said. "My teacher said only today that there is nothing that is so good that it cannot be made better, if we will only try. I think there may be better ways of making soup than our old way. Make the soup tonight *without tomatoes,* Mama!"

"No tomatoes?" Mama said. "And no beans? In Mexicali Soup?" Mama looked at the thoughtful face of Juan and at the thoughtful face of Manuel. Then she closed the bags of groceries carefully. She walked away from the play street.

"We will be hungry for your soup tonight, Mama!" Juan said.

Manuel called, "Mama! You make the best soup in the world!"

At home, Mama put the groceries on the table. She sang a little song that only she could hear. She stood looking at the food. No potatoes. No peppers. Tomatoes—Mama pushed the tomatoes aside. Beans—she pushed the beans aside. Mama sat down and looked at what was left. "Well," Mama said. "The soup will be a little thinner tonight."

The door opened and closed. Rosa, the young woman of the family, came in. "Hello, Mama. Oh, Mama—I hope I'm in time! I heard you were making—" She looked at the groceries on the table. "All the way home I heard it. The boys and Maria—they all told me—and Mama! I want to ask you—please! *No garlic.*"

"Listen, Mama. Last night, when my friend took me to dinner, I had such fine soup! The place was so beautiful, Mama. And no garlic at all in the soup!"

"Just leave out the garlic," Rosa said, hugging Mama. "You make the best soup in the world."

A deep voice and many other voices called all at once.

"Mama! We are home, Mama!"

Then all of them, Juan and Manuel and Pablo, with Maria holding Papa by the hand —all of them came to stand in the doorway. Papa reached for the baby.

"I have heard of something special," Papa said. "I have heard we are having Mexicali Soup tonight."

Mama said nothing. But there was fire in Mama's eyes. She waited.

"Your soup, Mama . . ." Papa said. "It is the best soup in the world!"

"But you want me to leave out something? The corn, maybe? You want me to make my Mexicali Soup without the corn?" Mama asked.

"Corn?" Papa opened his hands wide. "What is corn? It is a little nothing! Put it in or leave it out," he said, hugging Mama. "It does not matter. The soup will be just as—"

"Enough!" Mama said. "Out of here—all of you!" Mama waved her arms wide in the air. There was fire in Mama's eyes again. "I have work to do. Go."

"But, Mama," said Rosa, "we always help you with—"

"No!" Mama said. "Out!"

Rosa and Juan and Manuel, Pablo and Maria, and Papa with the baby went away to the living room.

There was no sound coming from Mama. Then, the sound of a quiet song. Soon they heard the good sounds of the table being set for dinner.

Mama was singing a happy song from the old home in the mountains. Juan and Manuel, Pablo and Maria, and Rosa and Papa looked at one another and smiled. Mama was singing.

Then Mama's voice called to them. "The soup is ready. Come and eat now."

"Ah! That is what I like to hear," said Papa, jumping up with the baby. "The soup is ready before I have even started to smell it cooking."

"*Mmm-mmm!*" said Juan and Manuel, running for the big table.

"*Mmm-mmm!*" said Maria and Pablo and Rosa when they saw the hot soup on the table. "Our Mama makes the best soup in the world."

But what was the matter?

"This doesn't look like Mexicali Soup," said Maria, looking at the bowl before her.

"It doesn't smell like Mexicali Soup," said Pablo.

Juan put down his spoon.

Manuel put down his spoon.

"This is not Mexicali Soup," said Rosa. "This is nothing but hot water!"

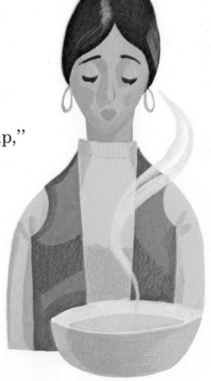

Everyone looked at Mama. Mama smiled and sang the old song from the mountains.

"Did you forget to bring the soup, Mama?" asked Papa.

"No," Mama said, still smiling. "This is the soup. And it is just what you wanted. I made the soup the way my family asked me to make it.

"I left out the potatoes that Maria does not want. I left out the peppers that Pablo does not want. I left out the beans that Manuel does not want. I left out the tomatoes that Juan does not want. For Rosa, I left out the garlic. And for Papa, I left out the corn, the little nothing that does not matter.

"The **new** Mexicali Soup!
It is so quick! So easy
to make," Mama said. "You just
leave everything out of it."

Joe

We feed the birds in winter,
And outside in the snow
We have a tray of many seeds
For many birds of many breeds
And one gray squirrel named Joe.

But Joe comes early,
Joe comes late,
And all the birds
Must stand and wait.
And waiting there for Joe to go
Is pretty cold work in the snow.

—David McCord

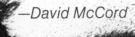

Elisabeth, the Bird Watcher

Felice Holman

Elisabeth looked out the window and saw a chickadee standing in the snow.

"Papa," said Elisabeth. "She's looking for something to eat. Do you think we could build a bird feeder and take care of her for the winter?"

"Good idea!" Papa said.

After lunch, Elisabeth and her father began to build the bird feeder. When they were through, they hung the feeder on the sill of the picture window.

"We can watch the birds while they eat," said Elisabeth. "I'll put out some bread."

"Well," began her father. "Some birds like bread, but let's get some sunflower seeds. Chickadees and some of the other smaller birds like sunflower seeds best. We can get some corn for the larger birds."

Elisabeth and her father went to the feed store. When they got home, Elisabeth put the seeds and the corn in the feeder. Then she called, *"All right, birds, come and get it!"*

She went into the house and stood at the window and waited and waited. But not one bird came near the feeder.

"They must be shy," Elisabeth said.

"The birds might come if we stand where they can't see us," Papa said.

That turned out to be a good idea. In a few minutes the first chickadee flew down to the feeder. She picked up a seed and flew to a nearby tree, where she put down the seed. Then she made a hole in the shell with her bill. She took the seed out of the shell, ate it, dropped the shell on the ground, came back, and snatched another seed.

"Oh, Papa, our bird feeder is working!" whispered Elisabeth.

"Here comes another bird," said Papa.

A big blue jay landed on the feeder. Unlike the chickadee, the blue jay just sat there eating and eating. He was very beautiful, but he ate too much.

"Save some seeds for the other birds," cried Elisabeth. The blue jay must have heard her, for he flew quickly to a tree.

In a minute a beautiful red cardinal came and sat in the bushes under the window. The cardinal looked at the feeder, but he didn't fly up to it. He flew to the ground. Then he ate seeds that the chickadee and the blue jay had knocked off the feeder.

"A cardinal would rather eat on the ground than from a feeder," Papa told Elisabeth.

After a few days, the birds weren't so shy. Elisabeth found she could stand very close to the window while they came to the feeder.

One morning while Elisabeth was still in bed, she heard a loud noise outside. She ran to the window and saw a big fat squirrel on the bird feeder. He was eating the sunflower seeds as fast as he could.

Elisabeth knocked on the window. The squirrel jumped off the feeder in surprise and ran away.

"What's all the noise?" Papa asked as he came into the living room.

"A squirrel was eating the bird food!" cried Elisabeth.

"We'll have to keep him out of the bird feeder," said Papa. "I'll cut the tops of the bushes so that he can't jump from them to the feeder."

Elisabeth put nuts on the ground for the squirrel while her father cut the tops of the bushes.

But the next morning Elisabeth and her father saw the squirrel on the feeder again. "What are we going to do?" Elisabeth asked her father.

"I've got an idea," said her father. "We won't put any seeds in the feeder at night. If the squirrel comes before we get up in the morning, he won't find anything to eat."

The next morning Elisabeth filled the feeder with seeds and corn. As she and her father stood and watched, the chickadees came to the feeder. Papa caught sight of the squirrel sitting in a nearby tree.

"You're too late, old boy," Papa said to the squirrel. "The birds got here first."

As he turned to go into the house, Elisabeth cried, "Papa! Look!" Papa turned around just in time to see the squirrel land on the feeder and start eating the seeds.

"That does it!" said Papa. "Come on, Elisabeth. We'll keep that squirrel out yet."

Papa and Elisabeth got some wire and put it across the tops of the bushes under the window.

"When the squirrel sees that wire, he won't come near the feeder," Papa said.

But the squirrel came the next morning. When Elisabeth saw him eating the seeds in the feeder, she ran to tell her father.

"*What!*" yelled her father. "How did he get through the wire?" He ran to the window and knocked on it. He saw the squirrel jump in surprise and squeeze through one of the holes in the wire.

"That squirrel really surprised me," said Papa. "I didn't think he could squeeze through those holes. Well, I'll fix *that!*"

Papa got some wire with smaller holes. "I'd like to see the squirrel squeeze through this wire," he said.

The next morning Elisabeth and her father went to the big window. They were just in time to see the squirrel climb up the bushes and look at the wire.

They couldn't believe what they saw next. The squirrel hooked his paws into the little holes and started to walk upside down along the bottom of the wire. He walked like this until he reached the top of the wire. He climbed over it, ran to the bird feeder, and snatched the seeds.

"I give up!" said Elisabeth.

But Papa had one more idea. He got a small basket and put some fine wire around it. He made a long loop with the wire. Then he put a nail into the window frame to hold the wire loop. He hung the basket right in the middle of the big window. Elisabeth filled the basket with seeds.

When the squirrel came the next morning, he climbed to the window sill. He looked up at the basket and tried a few jumps to reach it. The basket was too high. Then he tried to climb the glass. But his little paws couldn't hold on to it. He climbed up the window frame until he got as high as the basket. Holding on to the frame, he reached as far as he could across the glass with one of his paws. But the basket was just out of reach.

"Now we have him," said Elisabeth.

"But we'll do something for the squirrel," said Papa. "We'll take the old bird feeder that we made and . . ."

". . . fill it with food and put it on the ground for him," cried Elisabeth.

"Right," said Papa.

Elisabeth reached up and put some sunflower seeds into the basket. Then she called, "All right, birds, come and get it!"

These are some of the birds that Elisabeth saw:

Chickadees . . .
they have little black
caps and black bibs.

Blue Jays . . .
they are bright blue.
They are beautiful,
but they make a lot
of noise.

Cardinals . . .
the father is bright red,
and the mother is
a lovely light brown.
They make a chirping sound
and have a lovely whistle.

Downy Woodpeckers . . .
they have funny short
tails, and the father has
a red spot on his head.

Nuthatches . . .
they have black caps,
great long bills,
and climb upside down.

Mourning Doves . . .
they look like small grayish-
brown pigeons and make a
sad *cooo, cooo, cooo* sound.
They eat on the ground,
and when they fly, their
wings make a whistling sound.

Goldfinches and Purple Finches . . .
they don't peck seeds open
like chickadees, but crunch
them right in their beaks,
and then leave the shells
on the feeder.

The Practical Princess

Jay Williams

PART ONE
The Jewel Tree of Paxis

Princess Bedelia was as lovely as the moon on a clear summer night. She was as graceful as a cat leaping. Best of all, she was very practical.

When she was born, three wise old women had given her things they thought she could use as a princess. The first woman had given her beauty. The second one had given her grace. But the third one had said, "I give her common sense."

"I don't think much of that," said King Ludwig. "What good is common sense to a princess? All she needs is grace and beauty."

But when Bedelia grew up, something happened which made the king change his mind.

A dragon moved into the king's country. He found a dark cave on top of a mountain to live in. The first thing he did was to send a letter to the king. "I must have a princess to eat by tomorrow," the letter said. "Or I will kill all of you with the fire of my breath."

Sadly, King Ludwig called together his men and read them the letter.

"Maybe," said one of the men, "we had better look for a prince to kill the dragon. That is what is done in these cases most of the time."

"I'm afraid we haven't time," answered the king. "The dragon has only given us until tomorrow morning. There is no help for it. We will have to send him the princess."

"Why?" asked Princess Bedelia. "Dragons can't tell a princess from anyone else. Use your common sense."

"That may be so, but maybe this one can," said her father. "If we don't send you along, he'll kill us all."

"Right," said Bedelia. "I see I'll have to take care of this myself."

Bedelia left the room. She got the largest and brightest of her dresses and filled it with straw and tied it together with string. Into the middle of the bundle, she packed about a hundred pounds of gunpowder.

Bedelia got two big young men to carry it up the mountain for her. She stood at the opening of the cave and called, "Come out! Here is the princess!"

The dragon came out of the cave. Seeing the bright dress covered with gold and silver and hearing Bedelia's voice, he opened his mouth wide.

As Bedelia gave a sign, the two young men threw the dress filled with straw and gunpowder into the dragon's mouth. Bedelia threw herself on the ground, and the two young men ran.

As the gunpowder met the fire inside the dragon, there was a loud noise.

Bedelia got up and brushed herself off. "Dragons," she said, "are not very bright."

She went back to the castle for school. The class that morning was about nearby people and places. "North of our country is Istven," said the teacher. "Lord Garp, the ruler of Istven, is old and mean."

At that very minute, Lord Garp was coming to the castle. Word of Bedelia's killing of the dragon had reached him. "That girl," said he, "is just the wife for me."

The king sent for Bedelia. "My dear," he said, "just see who is here."

"I see. It's Lord Garp," said Bedelia. She turned to go.

"He wants to marry you," said the king.

Bedelia looked at Lord Garp. His face was old. He had only two teeth. Six long hairs grew from his ear, and not one on his head. She felt like crying.

But she said, "I'm very pleased. Thank you, Lord Garp. Just let me talk to my father for a minute."

Bedelia and the king went to another room. Bedelia said to the king, "What will Lord Garp do if I won't marry him?"

"He is mean and old," said the king, unhappily. "And he is used to having his own way in everything. He will be mad. He will most likely make war on us. Then there will be trouble."

"I see!" said Bedelia. "We must be practical."

She returned to the room where Lord Garp was and smiled at him. She said, "My lord, as you know, many times a princess sets a task for anyone who wishes to marry her. Surely, you could do a task for me."

"Name your task," said Lord Garp.

"Bring me," said Bedelia, "a branch from the Jewel Tree of Paxis."

Lord Garp said he would, and off he went. "I think," said Bedelia to her father, "that we have seen the last of him. Paxis is very far away, and wild animals watch over the Jewel Tree of Paxis."

PART TWO

The Volcano of Scoria

But in two weeks, Lord Garp was back. With him he had a chest, and from the chest he took a wonderful branch. Its bark was of gold. The leaves that grew from it were of fine silver. The branch was covered with flowers, and each flower had a jewel in the middle.

Bedelia's heart sank as she took the branch. But then she said to herself, "Use your common sense, my girl! Lord Garp never went that far in two weeks, and he isn't the man to fight his way through wild animals."

She looked carefully at the branch. Then she said, "My lord, you know that the Jewel Tree of Paxis is a living tree, even if it is all made of jewels."

"Why, of course," said Lord Garp. "Everyone knows that."

"Well," said Bedelia, "then why is it that these flowers have no smell?"

Lord Garp turned red.

"I think," Bedelia went on, "that this branch was made in Istven by men who are very good at setting jewels. Not very nice of you, my lord. Some people might even call it cheating."

"Never mind all that," he said. "Set me another task. This time, I will do it."

Bedelia took a deep breath. "Very well. Then bring me a coat made from the skins of animals who live in the Volcano of Scoria."

Lord Garp said he would, and off he went. "The Volcano of Scoria," said Bedelia to her father, "is covered with red-hot lava, and burns with a great fire. I think we have now seen the last of Lord Garp."

But in a week, Lord Garp was back. This time, he carried a coat that was as bright and red as fire. It was made of red animal skins put together with fine golden wire.

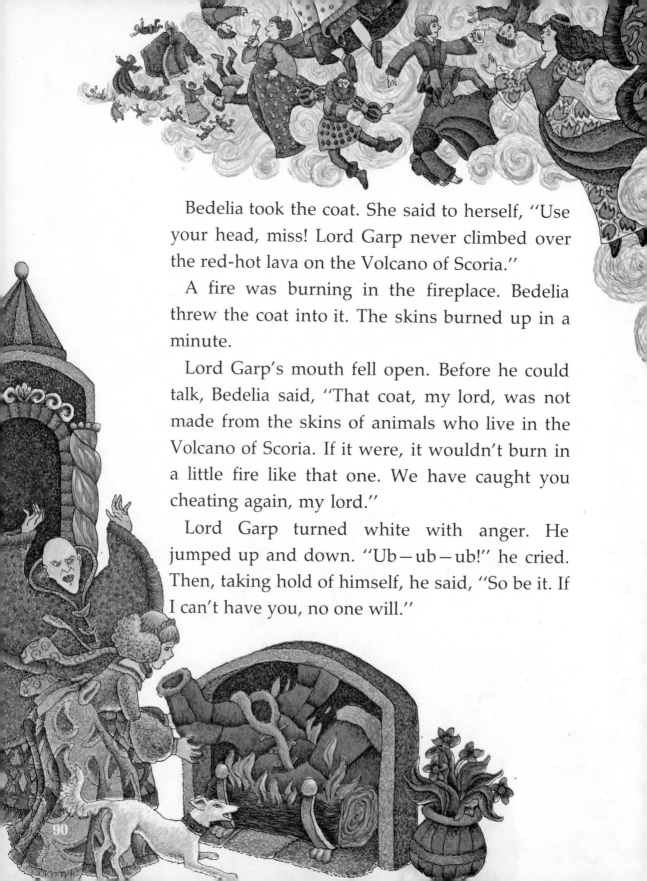

Bedelia took the coat. She said to herself, "Use your head, miss! Lord Garp never climbed over the red-hot lava on the Volcano of Scoria."

A fire was burning in the fireplace. Bedelia threw the coat into it. The skins burned up in a minute.

Lord Garp's mouth fell open. Before he could talk, Bedelia said, "That coat, my lord, was not made from the skins of animals who live in the Volcano of Scoria. If it were, it wouldn't burn in a little fire like that one. We have caught you cheating again, my lord."

Lord Garp turned white with anger. He jumped up and down. "Ub—ub—ub!" he cried. Then, taking hold of himself, he said, "So be it. If I can't have you, no one will."

Lord Garp touched his large ring. At once, a great wind came up. It sent King Ludwig flying one way and his men the other. Bedelia was picked up and carried off through the air. When she could get her breath and look about her, she found herself in a room at the top of a castle.

Bedelia looked out of the window. About the castle was flat land. She saw something far away. It came closer. It was Lord Garp on horseback.

He came to the castle and looked up at Bedelia. "Aha!" he said. "So you are safe and sound, are you? And will you marry me now?"

"Never," said Bedelia.

"Then stay there until never comes," said Lord Garp. Away he rode.

For the next two days, Bedelia felt very sorry for herself. Each day Lord Garp came and asked if she had changed her mind, and each day she said no. Her only hope was that, as sometimes happens in old stories, a prince might come riding by who would save her.

But on the third day, she gave herself a shake. "Now then, pull yourself together," she said. "If you sit waiting for a prince to save you, you may sit here forever. Be practical! If there's any saving to be done, you're going to have to do it yourself."

She jumped up. There was something she had not done, and now she did it. She tried the door.

It opened.

Outside were three other doors. But there was no sign of a stair or any way down from the top of the castle.

She opened two of the doors and found that they led into rooms just like hers. Behind the third door, however, lay what seemed to be a haystack.

Quietly she went closer. Then she saw that what she had thought was a haystack was in fact a large pile of blond hair. Pushing it aside, she found a young man, sound asleep.

Bedelia shook him. He opened his eyes and tried to sit up. But the pile of blond hair made this hard.

"Who are you?" Bedelia asked.

"I am Prince Perian," he said, "the real ruler of Istven. But Lord Garp tricked me into taking a pill which makes me very tired and makes me sleep most of the day."

He got to his feet, with a little help from Bedelia. "Oh!" he said. "Look how my hair and beard have grown. I've been here for years. Thank you, my dear. Who are you, and what are you doing here?"

Bedelia quickly told him the story.

"One more trick of Lord Garp's," he said. "We must get out of here and see that he does not get away with these bad deeds."

"Easier said than done," Bedelia said. "There is no stair in this castle, as far as I can tell, and the outside wall is much too flat to climb down."

"This will take some thought," Perian said. "What we need is a long rope."

"Use your common sense," said Bedelia. "We haven't any rope."

She laughed and said, "But we have your beard."

Perian knew her meaning at once and laughed. "I'm sure it will reach to the ground," he said. "But we haven't anything sharp to cut it off with."

"That is so," said Bedelia. "Hang it out the window and let me climb down. I'll search the castle, and maybe I can find a ladder or a stair. If nothing else works, I can go for help."

She and the prince gathered up the beard in their arms and went into Bedelia's room, which had the largest window.

Perian hung the beard out of the window and held it with his hands so that it wouldn't pull too much on his face. Bedelia climbed out of the window and slid down the beard.

But all at once, out of the forest came loud sounds, a cloud of dust, and then Lord Garp on his fast horse. With one look, he saw what was happening.

"I'll teach you to get in the way," Lord Garp yelled. He leaped from the horse and grabbed the beard. He gave it a great pull. Perian came out of the window headfirst. Down he fell and landed right on top of old Lord Garp.

This saved Perian, who was not hurt at all. But it was the end of Lord Garp.

Prince Perian and Princess Bedelia went back to Istven on Lord Garp's horse. In the great city the prince was met with a cry of joy—once everyone knew who he was, after so many years and under so much hair.

And, of course, since Bedelia had saved Perian from Lord Garp, she married Perian. First, however, she made him get a haircut and shave so that she could see what he really looked like. For she was always practical.

Watch the Sentence Grow!

You can start with a short sentence and add more and more information to make the sentence grow and change.

Children play.
Happy children play.
Happy children play and sing.
Happy children play games and sing songs.

You can make the sentence even longer by adding words that tell where, when, how, why. Add some of these words to the sentence and see how it changes.

at school	in the morning
on the stage	after school
all over town	at six o'clock

loudly	because it's fun
softly	so people can dance
proudly	because they like music

2 ANIMAL WORLD

Pleased to Meet You

A tiger with a hungry smile,
A large and scaly crocodile,
A grizzly bear with big, sharp claws,
A lion with enormous jaws
Would not be very nice to meet
If you were strolling down the street.

But when you see them in the zoo
Just smile, and ask them "How d' you do?"
Since they're locked IN and you're
         locked OUT
There's nothing to be scared about.

—*Norah Smaridge*

Mary Neville

The First and Last Annual Pet Parade

PART ONE

Something to Manage

In our town there had never been anything like a pet parade before. Some people said that the first annual pet parade got started the summer that firecrackers got ended.

Others said it wasn't the firecrackers. The parade got started because Mrs. Van Horn was looking for something to manage. There is plenty to manage in an annual pet parade.

My brother George and I were afraid to put our big dog in the parade because she hated cats. But we should have known that Mrs. Van Horn would have thought of that. Dogs would be together in one part of the parade. Between the dog part and the cat part would be goats, fish, and turtles. It is hard to fight a turtle.

The biggest pets would lead the parade. These would be horses and ponies. The littlest pets would follow. Do you wonder what they'd be? A bee? A butterfly?

Prizes were going to be given for the biggest, the littlest, the oldest, the youngest, and lots of other pets.

The parade would gather at the school, move across the bridge, over the river, and end at the library. Prizes would be given there.

An awful lot of dogs and cats were cleaned up around town that week. So were a few pigs — small ones.

The day came! George said, "Hurry up. Do you think they're going to hold up the parade till you get there?"

"No," I said.

Down on Washington Street it looked awfully full of people and animals. My brother George and I were in the dog part. We never did see the first part of the pet parade. But we could hear it. There were people yelling and animals tramping around up there. There were horses, I think, some ponies, a few burros, and a homesick sheep.

We were all waiting around in the middle of Washington Street, holding on to our animals. Our dog got to know the most dogs she ever had known at one time before.

At last we began to move. Slowly the pet parade moved on a little at a time. All the people along the street waved and called.

George and I never did see the back end of the pet parade. And it kept getting farther and farther back.

Just ahead of us, some little girls had their pet pigs in doll buggies. They were pushing the buggies. But it was hard for them to keep up.

Just behind us was George's friend, Herbie. He was getting tired of pulling his wagon with the cage of mice in it. By this time, our part of the parade was between Cherry and Maple Streets. We were getting closer to the bridge.

"I hope the bridge will hold the parade," I told George.

"Don't worry," said George. "The new bridge could hold a parade of elephants."

But George and I forgot something. The same thing about the bridge floor Mrs. Van Horn forgot!

Now the luckiest people in the pet parade were the pony riders who got to carry messages from the first part of the parade to the back. Just then one of these pony riders came tearing along and calling,

"Wait! Stop! Something awful is happening up ahead."

"Now what?" said George.

"It's the bridge!" someone called.

The thing we all forgot was the floor of the bridge. It had spaces in between for the snow to go through in winter. We found out that the animals with little feet would not go out on that bridge. Their feet would go right through the spaces in the bridge. They stopped. They wouldn't follow the big animals across the bridge. But the back end of the parade didn't get the message in time. And the parade started to pile

up

on

itself.

The dogs began snapping at each other. Cats were climbing up the trees. The big animals were going across the bridge and then coming back again with the others. And the scared little pigs jumped out of their doll buggies.

Mrs. Van Horn hurried by, and we heard her cry,

"We have lost control of our pet parade."

It was true.

What Happened Next
or
The Last Part of the Story

How the parade was ever going to get moving again, I didn't see. Soon all the animals would be after each other. Their owners would give up, and everyone would just go home. No prizes! No *nothing!*

I felt like crying. It was such a mess.

George said, "Try to keep smiling. A pet parade should be happy."

The police car had made it around the parade. The police were standing in the street, trying to get things moving.

Suddenly, around one corner into this mess came the ice-cream man's truck. Because of the noise, no one heard his bell. And around the other corner came Mr. J. P. Cutler in his big, black car. George and I knew what was going to happen one second before it did. They met!

CRASH!

ICE CREAM

Mr. J. P. Cutler climbed out and saw that there was not much of a dent in his big, black car. The ice-cream man looked sadly at the mess of ice cream all over the place. Ice cream on the sidewalk! Ice cream on the street! Ice cream on the bridge!

"Great!" George said. *"Hurry before it's melted."*

"Here, hold my mice," Herbie said to George. *"I'm going to get some ice cream for free!"*

"Hold your own mice," George told him. Then George looked at me. "It's your turn to hold the dog."

And he was off.

Then suddenly Mr. J. P. Cutler surprised everyone. "It is my pleasure—" he called out, "my great pleasure to ask each and every one of you to have some ice cream."

He waved some green money in the air. It made the ice-cream man smile.

And each and every one of us had ice cream.

Then the meat-eating animals were eating melted ice cream. And the plant-eating animals were eating melted ice cream.

How the parade got moving again was wonderful! Another police car came along. Mrs. Van Horn got out with all the blue, red, and gold prize ribbons.

Then Mrs. Van Horn ate some ice cream while Mr. J. P. Cutler held up his hand and said, "It will be my pleasure to give out prize ribbons as soon as we restore order."

George was back by me. So he gave me a push and said, "Why don't you be quiet and restore order?"

So I did. And everyone else began to restore order, too. Then the prize ribbons were given out.

People did say, however, that the firecrackers *might* have been more quiet.

Martha Sanders

Alexander and the Magic Mouse

PART ONE

The Old Lady

There was once an Old Lady who lived in a house on top of a hill. At the foot of the hill was a river. On the other side of the river was a town.

The Old Lady was never lonely, for she lived with her animal friends:

a Brindle Cat,

a Magic Mouse,

and an alligator

named Alexander.

When the Brindle Cat wasn't sitting in the sun, he was thinking about how to catch the Magic Mouse. But the Magic Mouse had made herself invisible. The Cat couldn't catch her.

112

Each day the Old Lady put out food for the Magic Mouse, and each day the Brindle Cat got ready to catch her. The Magic Mouse had been invisible for so long, though, that the Brindle Cat had really forgotten what to look for. So he always fell asleep.

On hot days Alexander would go down the hill to the river and swim near a sign the Old Lady had put up. It said,

That was to keep people away. Alexander wasn't dangerous at all though. He was really very gentle. But the Old Lady knew people would be scared of him. Alexander felt that if he smiled enough, people would know that he was gentle and not at all a dangerous animal.

Sometimes when he was swimming, he would stick his head out of the water to see if anyone was near. But the few people he saw always cried, *"Help!"* and ran away. That made Alexander very sad.

The animals all loved the Old Lady. When the Old Lady was young, she went to many faraway lands. She always came home with something different. That's how the Brindle Cat and Alexander the gentle alligator came to live with the Old Lady and the Magic Mouse.

The Magic Mouse came with the house. She had always been there.

Each afternoon at five o'clock, the animals came into the living room to have tea and cakes with the Old Lady. They told her what had happened that day.

The Brindle Cat had to promise not to try to catch the Magic Mouse while they were all having tea. Even though the Magic Mouse made herself invisible, she was never too sure of the Brindle Cat.

The Old Lady would put a bit of cake on the table near the yarn basket, and soon it would be gone.

Sometimes, as the cake disappeared, the Brindle Cat would forget himself and reach for the Magic Mouse. The Old Lady would look at him and say, "Now, now," and he would put his paws down again.

One fine afternoon in May, as they had all just sat down to tea, a little voice came from the yarn basket. Everyone was very surprised because the Magic Mouse was shy and didn't say much.

The Magic Mouse said,

> *"It is going to rain for*
> *thirty days and thirty nights!*
> *My tail tells me so,*
> *and my tail is always right.*
> *We must get ready!"*

The Old Lady got up and went to the window. There wasn't a cloud in the sky. "Are you sure?" she asked.

"My tail tells me so, and my tail is always right,"

said the Magic Mouse, and that was all she would say. Her feelings were hurt, so she wouldn't say when the storm would begin.

"Let us think," said the Old Lady, sitting down again. "We must have plenty of logs for the fire, plenty of candles, plenty of food, and plenty of books to read."

While Alexander got the logs and the Old Lady made sure there was enough food and candles, the Brindle Cat finished his cake and went to sleep.

The next morning it began to rain. By lunchtime the drops were coming down hard and fast. Alexander made a fire and the Old Lady read stories out loud. From time to time they looked out the window at the rain. *What a wonderful storm!*

But in the middle of the night the Old Lady jumped out of bed to light a candle and went downstairs to the living room. "Magic Mouse, Magic Mouse!" she whispered.

"*Yes?*" answered the Magic Mouse in a sleepy voice.

"Do you think the people in the town know it's going to rain for thirty days and thirty nights? Surely the river will flood the town," said the Old Lady.

"*No one knows but us,*" said the Magic Mouse.

"We must tell the people in the town about the flood," the Old Lady said at breakfast the next day.

She put on her dress and went quickly out the door. But soon she was back. "It's too muddy out there."

"You could write a letter," said the Brindle Cat, "and I'll go."

"Yes, yes, a letter to the Mayor," said the Old Lady. She wrote:

Dear Mr. Mayor:
  I am sorry to tell you that it is going to rain for thirty days and thirty nights and the river will surely flood your town. You must think how to stop it.
        Your neighbor,
The Old Lady on Top of the Hill

The Brindle Cat took the letter and went out into the rain. But soon he was back. "The water has covered the bridge and I can't get across the river," he said.

"Then I'll go," said Alexander, "for I can swim any river."

"Be very careful, Alexander," said the Old Lady. She put the letter in his mouth, and off he went.

PART TWO

The Silver Medal

Alexander slid down the muddy hill, right into the river. He began to swim, holding his head up high so the letter wouldn't get wet.

He swam as hard as he could, but the river was very strong. As he swam, Alexander didn't think he was strong enough to get across the river. He was frightened and trembling. But he kept on swimming, and soon he reached the other side.

But where was the town? He had been carried right by it! Now he had to walk back. It was a long way, and Alexander wasn't used to walking, even a little way. He walked along slowly, tired from his hard swim. At last he saw the town.

A man with an umbrella was hurrying down the street through the rain. Alexander went up to him. He smiled and asked where the Mayor lived. But the man dropped his umbrella and ran down the street trembling and yelling.

"HELP!

HELP!"

The man made Alexander very sad. Then he saw a woman. He smiled at her, but she dropped her umbrella and ran inside a store. Other people ran away when they saw Alexander. The alligator was left all alone. He sat down on the sidewalk, and tears rolled down his face.

Soon a little boy came along. Alexander smiled at him through his tears. The little boy stopped.

He said, "Hello! What's the matter?"

"Hello," said Alexander. "I've got to find someone who will give this letter to the Mayor. Do you know where he lives?"

"Yes," said the boy. "He lives at the end of the street."

"Would you give him this letter?" Alexander asked.

"Sure," said the boy, as he reached into Alexander's mouth.

"Oh, thank you so much," said Alexander. "Don't forget."

"I won't. Goodbye!" cried the boy.

Meanwhile, in the house on top of the hill, the Old Lady walked up and down, up and down. Night had come, and still Alexander had not come home. "Where can he be?" she asked. The animals were quiet.

"I'm hungry," said the Brindle Cat. "Let's have dinner."

After dinner the Cat went to sleep. The Old
Lady kept going to the door and looking out
into the rainy night. At last it was time for bed.
But the Old Lady could not sleep. She got up in
the middle of the night and went downstairs to
the living room.

"Magic Mouse, Magic Mouse!" the Old
Lady whispered. "Is Alexander safe?"

"*I think so,*" said the Magic Mouse in a sleepy
little voice.

It was still raining the next morning. The Old Lady went up to the roof of her house and looked through her telescope. At first she could see nothing but rain. Then she thought she saw people building something—a wall made of bags of sand! So the Mayor did get her letter!

But where in the world was Alexander? She looked through the telescope all morning, but there was no sign of Alexander. The Brindle Cat had to go up to the roof to tell her it was lunchtime.

In the afternoon the Old Lady looked through her telescope and saw an awful thing. The sandbag wall was higher, but the river was higher, too. Which would win, the wall or the river?

By five o'clock it was too dark to see anymore. The Old Lady was just about to call everyone to tea when she heard a sound at the door. She ran to the door and there was Alexander!

He was muddy and cold and tired and hungry. As soon as he got inside, he began sneezing and trembling. *"Quickly! A cloth and some hot tea!"* cried the Old Lady. They dried him off, gave him some tea and some dinner, and put him to bed. But Alexander kept on sneezing. No one would say so, but everyone was very worried. Alexander was sick.

The next morning the Old Lady went to look through her telescope. She saw a big wave coming down the river. The flood! It came closer and closer. But the townspeople had made the wall very high. The Old Lady took a deep breath. The wave came to the wall and almost went right over the top—but it didn't! The wall was strong enough to hold back the water. The town would be safe! The Old Lady went to tell Alexander the news.

Alexander was still sneezing. The Old Lady felt his head. It was very hot. "Oh dear!" she said.

"Oh, dear, oh dear," said the Brindle Cat, who had come to see how Alexander was. But the Magic Mouse could not be found.

That night the Old Lady sat beside Alexander's bed. At last she got up and went downstairs. "Magic Mouse, Magic Mouse," she whispered. "How can I help Alexander?"

"Look on the tea table," said the Magic Mouse in a sleepy voice.

There lay a little cake with writing on it. It said,

"Oh, thank you, Magic Mouse!" whispered the Old Lady. She went up to Alexander's room and put the cake inside his mouth. As he swallowed it, he smiled, thinking it was teatime.

The next morning it was as rainy as ever, but Alexander felt much better. After breakfast he and the Brindle Cat played a game. The Old Lady was watching the river and the wall through her telescope. The town looked safe.

Every day it rained and rained and rained. The Old Lady was running out of food. The Brindle Cat was tired of playing games. Even the Magic Mouse was tired of sitting around and ate a hole in the yarn basket.

One day the Old Lady got out of bed with a funny feeling. Something was different. It was very quiet outside. Then she knew. The rain had stopped.

It wasn't long before the river got smaller. The townspeople took away the sandbags and began building a new bridge. Soon the great rain and the flood were almost forgotten.

One summer afternoon the Old Lady and the animals heard some lovely music. When they opened the door, they saw the Mayor and the townspeople.

The Mayor began his speech. "Dear Lady, you were not forgotten," he said. "The townspeople and I want to thank you for what you did. I wish to give you this silver medal."

"Oh, no, it's not for me, it's for Alexander!" said the Old Lady. As she gave the medal to Alexander, she told the Mayor about the night that Alexander swam the river.

The Mayor and the townspeople stayed for tea. Everyone told Alexander how brave he was. After they all had left, the Old Lady looked at Alexander. "It's a lovely medal!" she said to him.

"What's so great about a medal?" the Brindle Cat said. He was jealous, of course.

Alexander looked at his medal in the mirror and smiled. Tears of joy ran down his face. And inside the yarn basket the Magic Mouse smiled, too.

THE WINNER!

These animals were all winners in a pet show. What is special about each one? Read the words below.

<u>bigger</u> <u>smaller</u> <u>softer</u> <u>slower</u>

All the underlined words end with *er*. When we compare two things, we often add *er* to words. Look at the pets above. What pet is *bigger* than a cat? *smaller* than a turtle? *softer* than a horse? *slower* than a grasshopper?

Why did each pet win a prize? Read the words below.

<u>biggest</u> <u>smallest</u> <u>softest</u> <u>slowest</u>

All the underlined words end with *est*. When we compare two things, we often add *est* to words. What pet is *biggest? smallest? softest? slowest?* What pet might win a prize for being *fastest? smartest? strongest?*

Bernice Myers

How to Find the Alligator You've Always Wanted and What to Do with Him Then

If the one thing
in the whole world you've
always wanted is an alligator,
then here is how to get one.
You don't even have to leave home.

You can send away for it.

As soon as the box comes,
open it. But be careful.
When you throw
away the stuffing from
the box, make sure you don't
throw away the little bird inside.
The bird is the alligator's toothpick.
He always sits on the alligator's back.

Now that you have the alligator,
what will you do with him?

While he is small,
he will make a nice pet.
Children you never saw before
will want to play with you.
It's a great find for
show-and-tell.
It's great for your
science project, too.

After you have him for
a while, you will notice
that he is getting bigger
and bigger.

133

Soon he will be so big
that you will no longer
be able to take him for a walk,
have him sleep in the bathtub,
or hide him
from Grandma.

Don't be too sad.
He can still be a lot of laughs
around the house.
Stand him up in the corner
near the door on rainy nights.
Put him on the floor near the
fireplace.
Show him to friends who
come to visit and then
stay too late.
They will leave almost at once—
sometimes forgetting to take
their hats and coats
and other things
with them.

An alligator makes a good
hiding place.

Try hiding there when you
drop cake
or paint on the rug.
No one will ever think
of looking for you
in an alligator.

Just make sure he's already
had his breakfast.

The Spangled Pandemonium

The Spangled Pandemonium
Is missing from the zoo.
He bent the bars the barest bit,
And slithered glibly through.

He crawled across the moated wall,
He climbed the mango tree,
And when his keeper scrambled up,
He nipped him in the knee.

To all of you, a warning
Not to wander after dark,
Or if you must, make very sure
You stay out of the park.

For the Spangled Pandemonium
Is missing from the zoo,
And since he nipped his keeper,
He would just as soon nip you!

—Palmer Brown

With or Without?

The suffixes *ful* and *less* are added to words to change their meanings. The suffix *ful* means *full of*. The suffix *less* means *without*.

The girl felt <u>hopeful</u>. The girl felt <u>hopeless</u>. The girl felt <u>joyful</u>. The girl felt <u>joyless</u>.

Which of the underlined words means *full of hope? full of joy?*

Which of the underlined words means *without hope? without joy?*

Match these four words to the pictures below.

careful   thoughtless

careless   thoughtful

A Walrus Named Boris

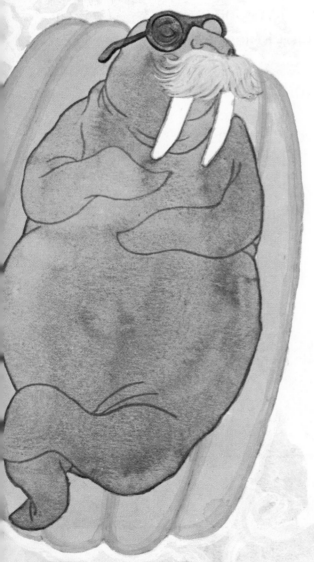

Bernice Myers

A walrus named Boris
Lived in a zoo,
And much of the time
He had nothing to do.

He would swim in the water
And sit in the sun
And jump for a fish
Just to please everyone.

Thought Boris, "How sad
To sit here all day.
I'd take Herman's place
Anytime...right away!

"I'd like to be Herman
and take care of the zoo.
I'd work all day long.
And have plenty to do."

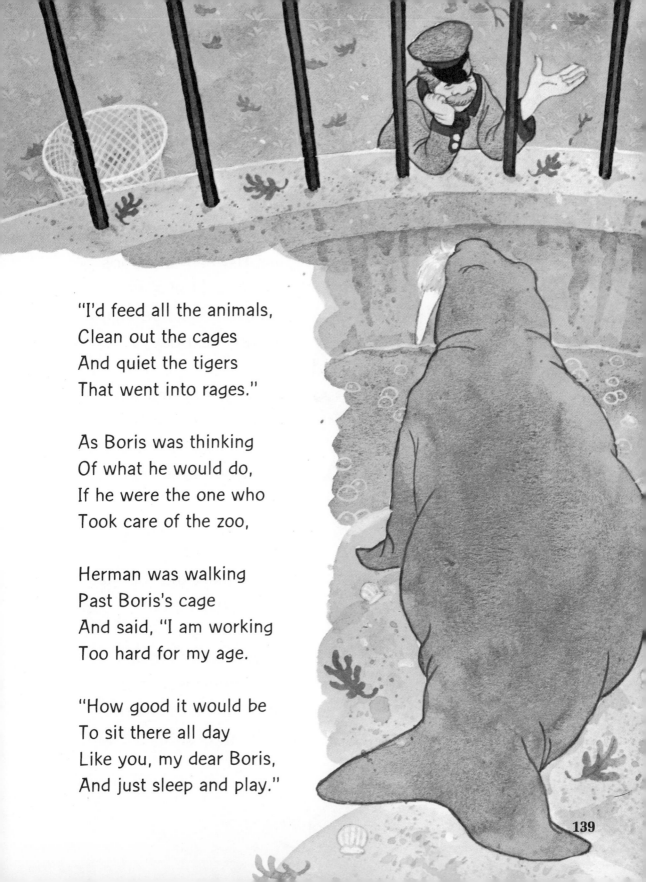

"I'd feed all the animals,
Clean out the cages
And quiet the tigers
That went into rages."

As Boris was thinking
Of what he would do,
If he were the one who
Took care of the zoo,

Herman was walking
Past Boris's cage
And said, "I am working
Too hard for my age.

"How good it would be
To sit there all day
Like you, my dear Boris,
And just sleep and play."

139

Then Herman told Boris
He'd thought of a way
That each could be happy
The very next day.

And early next morning
The whole zoo could see
It was Boris, not Herman,
Outside with the key.

And inside the cage
On a rock in the sun,
Old Herman, the zoo man,
Just sat having fun.

The walrus was happy
And Herman was, too,
But the animals weren't,
"We'll move from the zoo!"

140

Boris tried to work fast
But then supper was late
And cleaning the cages
Would just have to wait.

The monkeys were starving
They leaped up and down,
The camels were angry
And ran all around.

The flies and the fleas
Moved in by the dozens,
They liked it so much
They called all their cousins.

"It's not all the fun
I thought it would be,"
Said Boris. "This zoo is
Just too much for me."

Boris got rid of
The flies and the fleas.
At last he could rest
And he dropped to his knees.

When Boris had done
All his work for the day,
He wanted to sleep.
But where could he stay?

So he said to himself,
"If I just use my head,
I think I could sleep
In Herman's big bed."

He knew Herman's house
Was not far away.
Thought Boris, "How long
Will his wife let me stay?"

"If I say very little
And try not to fight,
She'll think that I'm Herman
We look quite alike."

He climbed up the stairs
And opened the door.
"Dad!" children shouted.
There were dozens, or more.

"Sit down here, my love,"
Herman's wife said to Boris,
"And see what a supper
I've just cooked up for us."

He sat down to supper
And still no one knew
That in place of their daddy
Sat a walrus in blue.

143

He was sitting quite still
When he saw on a dish
A most happy sight —
A big beautiful fish!

Now Boris was starving.
He'd been waiting all day
For the smell of that fish
That came floating his way.

With one great big jump
He leaped out of his chair
And ate that big fish
In one bite...in mid-air.

That gave him away,
And the wife shouted, "Oh, my!
This isn't my Herman.
It's some other guy!"

144

The discovered Boris
Leaped right to the floor,
Ran out of the house,
And slammed the big door.

But looking behind him,
He saw the wife and brood,
And Boris the walrus
Had a change of mood.

Poor Boris thought, "Oh,
To be back in my cage.
This is clearly no life
For a walrus my age."

But Boris ran on
Till he came to the zoo.
He ran to his cage.
"I've had it! I'm through!"

"Herman, open this door,"
Shouted Boris. "Be quick!
Your wife and your children
Are making me sick!"

Boris got back in his cage,
Slammed the door,
And in no time at all,
Fell asleep on the floor.

But when Herman's wife
Saw Herman there, too,
She knew what had happened
That day at the zoo.

When Herman looked out
And saw his dear wife,
He was never so dismayed
In all of his life.

He could see she was laughing.
She thought it was fun.
"Well, my dear Herman,
Now look what you've done!"

"You may as well stay
And sleep under the stars.
We'll stay here, too —
But not behind bars."

That's how Boris found out
That his life at the zoo
Was better by far
With nothing to do.

Now he swims in the water
And sits in the sun
And jumps for a fish
Just to please everyone.

Rita Golden Gelman

Strange Company

THE PLAYERS

Announcer
Suzy, a three-year-old girl
Carmen, an eight-year-old girl
Kim, a friend
Tony, another friend
Brontosaurus
Mrs. Di Luca, the landlady
Mrs. Sanchez, Carmen's mother
Mr. Sanchez, Carmen's father
Mrs. Thompson, a teacher

OTHER FRIENDS

Jenny
Joshua
Bobby
Jan
Mitchell
Sarah
Kenny
Caroline
Penny

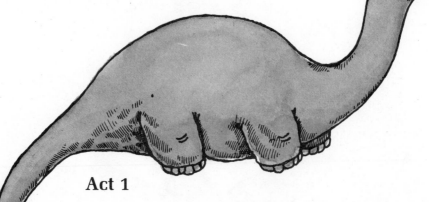

Act 1

TIME: One morning.
PLACE: Carmen's living room.

Announcer *(facing the audience).* This play is brought to you by . . .

Suzy *(walks on stage and up to the* **Announcer***).* Could I be in your play?

Announcer. You? You're three years old.

Suzy. I could say my numbers: 1, 2, 3, 5, 6.

Announcer. Go home, Suzy. You're too little. (**Suzy** *exits.*) As I was saying, this play is brought to you by ——————. Act 1 takes place in Carmen's living room, one morning.

(Exits.)

*(***Carmen** *and* **Kim** *are sitting on the floor, holding a sign:* **CARMEN AND KIM, PRIVATE DETECTIVES. WE SOLVE PROBLEMS.***)*

149

Carmen. What good are private detectives without any cases? We need some problems to solve. We'll never make any money this way.

Kim. Maybe we should sell cookies.

Carmen. Ugh. We've done that before. I want to do something new and exciting. *(Doorbell rings.)* Maybe this is something new and exciting now. *(Opens door.)* It's only Tony from upstairs.

Tony *(comes in with a big bundle and starts talking without taking a breath).* Carmen, I have to talk to you. Your mother and father are upstairs visiting, so I raced down here. Something has happened, and I don't know what to do. You've got to help me! I need a private detective. Are you still solving problems?

Carmen. Yes, yes, yes. Slow down. Something is missing. Right? Tell us what you've lost.

Tony. No, it's not what I've lost. It's what I've found! You see, when I got up this morning, I had company . . . right in the middle of my room.

Carmen. Company? What kind of company?

Tony. It was a . . . It was a . . . I think you'd
better look for yourself.

(**Tony** *opens bundle and points to a five-*
foot-high Brontosaurus.)

Kim. It's alive. It's a Brontosaurus and it's
alive.

Carmen. It's really alive. I can't believe it.

Tony. I didn't either. I thought I was dreaming,
so I went back to sleep. But when I got
up, it was still there.

*(**Suzy** sneaks in from side and lies down on the floor.)*

Carmen.   Suzy, what are you doing here?

Suzy.   I'm being in the play.

Carmen.   What are you?

Suzy.   I'm a rug.

Kim.   Get out of here!

Suzy   *(shouting numbers as she leaves).* 1, 2, 3, 4, 6.

Tony.   My big problem is the landlady. If she catches me with Brontosaurus, she'll throw my whole family out.

Kim.   Hmmmmm. How do you hide a Brontosaurus?

Carmen   *(looking out window at back).* Uh, oh! We're about to find out. Here comes the landlady now. *(Doorbell rings.)* Just a minute. I'll be right there. Hurry, let's put Brontosaurus in the bedroom.

*(They push **Brontosaurus** into bedroom on left side of stage.)*

Carmen   *(opening door).* Hello, Mrs. Di Luca.

Mrs. Di Luca.   Hello, Carmen. Your mother and father home?

Carmen. No, they're upstairs. But they should be back soon.

(*Bedroom door opens.* **Brontosaurus** *comes out.* **Kim** *and* **Tony** *try to get her back into the bedroom, but they can't. They try, without luck, to hide her.*)

Mrs. Di Luca. Oh, well. I'll see them later.

Carmen (*trying to turn* **Mrs. Di Luca** *away from* **Brontosaurus**). Well, it's been nice talking to you. I won't keep you any longer. You must have a lot to do.

Mrs. Di Luca.   Tell me, Carmen, how is school?

Carmen.   Oh, fine, Mrs. Di Luca, just fine. I'm sorry you have to go.

Mrs. Di Luca.   Yes. I guess I better. *(Exits.)*

Tony.   She didn't *say* anything!

Kim.   She didn't *do* anything!

Tony.   Maybe she's going to call the police.

Kim.   Carmen, your mother and father! We don't have time to . . .
(Door opens.)

Mrs. Sanchez.   Hello, children. What's new?
(Brontosaurus *pushes past* **Mr. Sanchez.)**

154

Carmen. Nothing much. Did you have fun?

Mr. Sanchez. Yes, thank you. Carmen, have you asked your friends if they want lunch? There's cheese or jelly for sandwiches.

Mrs. Sanchez. Have some milk, too.

Tony. Good idea. I'm hungry.

Kim. Me, too.

Mr. Sanchez. Mom and I have some work to do, so help yourselves. See you later.

(**Mr.** *and* **Mrs. Sanchez** *exit.*)

Tony. *They* didn't say anything either!

Carmen. I've got it. It's great! Don't you see? Brontosaurus is invisible to adults. Only kids can see her.

Kim. But she's so real. I mean, we can touch her and see her and feel her.

Tony. How can *we* see her and they can't?

Carmen. Don't ask me. I only know that the adults can't see Brontosaurus. (**Suzy** *comes in.*) What are you doing here?

Suzy. I'm hungry and I heard somebody say there was cheese and milk.

Kim. Suzy, get out of here.

Suzy *(leaving).* 1, 3, 4, 5, 6.

(**Brontosaurus** *lies down.*)

Kim. Something's the matter with Brontosaurus.

Tony. Maybe she's sick.

Carmen. Maybe she's hungry.

Tony. I tried to give her some eggs this morning, but she wouldn't eat.

Kim. Brontosauruses don't eat eggs; they eat ferns.

Carmen. Well, we don't have any ferns. So we'll have to find something else.

Tony.   How about cheese and milk?

Carmen.   We can try. *(Exits.)*

Kim.   Don't worry, Brontosaurus, we'll find something you can eat.

Tony.   You're going to love cheese and milk. You'll be so happy.

Carmen *(coming in with dish and glass).* Come on, Brontosaurus, *we* like it.
(They all take a bite; then offer it to **Brontosaurus.** *She turns away.)*

Carmen.   No. She doesn't like cheese and milk.

Tony.   Well, what'll we do? She's got to eat.

Carmen.   We'll try every kind of food there is until we find something that Brontosaurus likes. Go home and call everyone you know and tell them to bring over some food. We'll meet here at three.

Act 2

TIME: Three o'clock in the afternoon.
PLACE: Carmen's living room.

Announcer.   Act 2 takes place in . . .
(**Suzy** *walks on and off the stage, waving.*
Announcer *stops talking and watches until she is off.*) Act 2 takes place in Carmen's living room at three o'clock in the afternoon.
(**Carmen, Tony,** *and* **Kim** *are sitting in living room, waiting for company.* **Jenny, Joshua,** *and* **Bobby** *come in.*)

Carmen.   Hello, come on in.

Joshua   *(looking at sick* **Brontosaurus***).* Boy!

Jenny.   We thought you were fooling.

Bobby.   I brought chocolate cookies. *(Walks toward* **Brontosaurus,** *holding out cookie.*) She won't bite me, will she?

Carmen.   No. But I hope she bites the cookie.
(**Brontosaurus** *turns away from cookie.* **Bobby** *puts bag on floor, toward back.*)

Joshua.   She has to like chocolate cake.
Everybody likes chocolate cake.
(**Brontosaurus** *turns away from it.* **Joshua** *places bowl near cookies.*)

Jenny. Well, lettuce is a lot like ferns, and if I were a Brontosaurus, I'd eat lettuce.

*(***Brontosaurus*** *shakes her head at the lettuce.* ***Jan, Mitchell,*** *and* ***Sarah*** *come in.* ***Suzy*** *comes in and eats the chocolate cake, without being seen. Then she sits down on the other side of the room.)*

Mitchell. Here, Bronti. Have some peanuts.

*(***Brontosaurus*** *turns away from the peanuts.)*

Sarah. I brought *arroz con pollo.*

*(***Brontosaurus*** *turns away from the arroz con pollo.)*

Jan. How about peanut butter and jelly?

*(***Brontosaurus*** *shakes her head.)* She doesn't like peanut butter and jelly either.

Carmen. Look! The chocolate cake is gone. She must have eaten it. Hooray, Brontosaurus likes chocolate cake.

Everyone *(jumping around and shouting).* Hooray. She likes it.

Carmen *(outshouting everyone).* Wait. Stop. Quiet. *(Everyone stops talking.* **Carmen** *pulls* **Suzy** *to middle of stage.)* Look what I found.

Kim. Her face is covered with chocolate cake.

Everyone *(together).* Ooooooh.

Tony. Suzy, get out of our play.

Suzy. *(shouting as she leaves).* 1, 2, 4, 5, 6.

*(***Kenny** *and* **Caroline** *come in.)*

Kenny. I bet Brontosaurus is going to love corn on the cob. *(She turns away.)*

Mitchell. Oh, well. I guess we'll have to eat the corn on the cob ourselves.

(Everyone takes some corn on the cob.)

Kim. What did you bring, Caroline?

Caroline. Ice cream with chocolate syrup.

Everyone. Mmmmmm.

Caroline. . . . hot chocolate syrup.

Everyone. Mmmmmm.

Caroline. Here, Brontosaurus.

*(***Brontosaurus** *shakes her head.)*

Carmen. She doesn't like anything.

Penny. *(As she enters,* **Brontosaurus** *charges at her.)* Help. She's going to kill me!

Carmen. No, Penny. She's after your bowl. What did you bring?

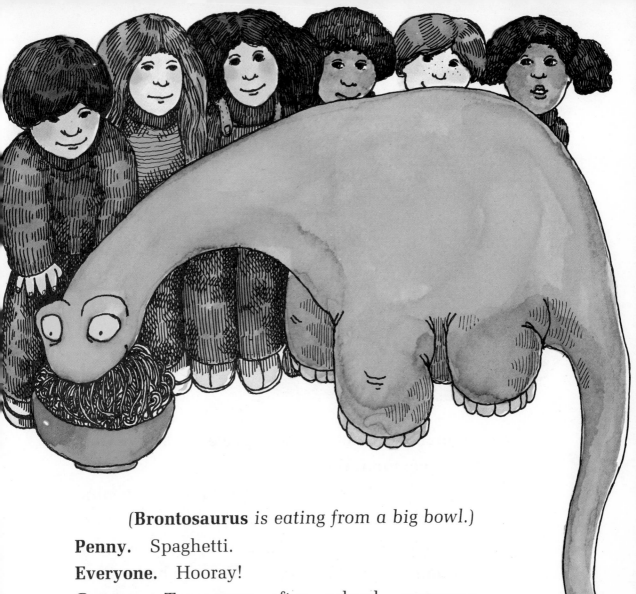

(**Brontosaurus** *is eating from a big bowl.*)

Penny. Spaghetti.

Everyone. Hooray!

Carmen. Tomorrow after school, everyone come over here with spaghetti.

Kim. Why don't we bring Brontosaurus to school? Then she could eat the spaghetti there.

Tony. To school? What'll Mrs. Thompson say?

Carmen. Mrs. Thompson won't say anything. Remember, she's an adult.

Act 3
TIME: Next morning
PLACE: School

Announcer.   Act 3 takes place in school the
next morning.
*(The stage has a few tables and chairs
placed to look like a classroom. All the
children but* **Suzy** *and* **Tony** *are on stage.)*

Joshua.   I brought a big bowl of spaghetti.

Everyone   *(taking bowls and pots from behind
their backs).* I did, too.

Tony   *(entering with* **Brontosaurus***).* We made
it. I kept thinking every adult would run
and shout. They never even looked. I
can't believe it!
(Children gather around **Brontosaurus**
who is eating from bowls on the floor.)

162

Mrs. Thompson *(comes in)*. What's all the noise? And what's in those bowls?

Sarah. Spaghetti.

Mrs. Thompson. Spaghetti? We can't have bowls of spaghetti all over the classroom. You'd better take them out to the playground.

Kenny. Oh, please, Mrs. Thompson. We can put them in the back.

Mrs. Thompson. No. Take them out.

Penny. But if we put them outside, they'll bring cats and dogs. The whole playground will be covered with animals.

Mrs. Thompson. Outside. All the spaghetti, all the bowls, and all the pots.
(The children leave. **Brontosaurus** *follows.)*

Mrs. Thompson. This is the strangest morning.
(The children return without **Brontosaurus.***)*

Kim. Where's Brontosaurus?

Tony. She won't leave the spaghetti.

Penny. What if she runs away?

Carmen. Then we'll have to look for her.

Mrs. Thompson. All right, class. Let's try to get down to a little work.

Act 4

TIME: Four o'clock in the afternoon,
                same day.

PLACE: Playground.

Announcer.   Act 4 takes place at four o'clock,
the same day, outside the school. *(Exits.)*
*(**Carmen** runs in from the right; **Tony** runs
in from the left. They run into each other
in the middle of the stage.)*

Tony.   Did you find her?

Carmen.   No. I looked everywhere.

Kim   *(running on).* It's no use. She's nowhere.
*(They all run off, calling. Each of the
other children runs across stage and off
the other way, calling* **Brontosaurus.***)*

Jenny.   Brontosaurus! Brontosaurus!

Kenny.   I've got some great spaghetti for you.

Sarah.   Here, Bronti. Here, Bronti. We love you.
(Others do the same.)
*(Slowly, the children return, still looking.
They stand in a line across the stage,
facing the audience.)*

Announcer. I'm afraid that's the end of our play. We've searched the whole town and found no Brontosaurus. We can't call the police because the police can't see Brontosaurus. And we can't ask our mothers and fathers for help. You (*points to audience*) are our only hope. If you find Brontosaurus, please feed her lots of spaghetti and call us at this number: 555-4126. (*Everyone unrolls a long paper with a telephone number on it.* **Suzy** *runs onto stage, points at each number, and says it aloud.*)

Suzy (*running off stage*). Hooray. I was in the play. I was in the play.

(THE END)

Working with Animals

Do you like animals? Would you like to study about them or take care of them? That's what these men and women do in their jobs.

This woman is the director of a nursery. But this nursery isn't in a hospital—it's in a zoo. The director cares for the baby animals until they are old enough to care for themselves. She feeds them and makes sure they are healthy. You can play with these babies at the children's zoo.

Porpoises are very smart animals. They even speak their own language. This man is a porpoise trainer. He takes care of the porpoises and teaches them to obey commands. To reward them for their work, he feeds them fish. This porpoise is thanking the trainer for the treat.

This woman is a zoo keeper. She takes care of the animals, feeds them, and makes sure they are in good health. Here, she is introducing an elephant to the visitors at the zoo.

This woman is a scientist at the zoo. In her job she studies all about animals. She learns where they live, what they eat, and how they care for themselves. What she learns about the different animals will help the trainers and zoo keepers take care of them.

Little House in the Big Woods

Laura Ingalls Wilder

About the Story

Long ago, much of our country was a wild land of deep woods, where few people lived. Laura Ingalls Wilder, who wrote the next story, knew what it was like to grow up in those days. She was born in 1867 in a little log house in the big woods. There she lived the first years of her life with her family — Ma, Pa, Mary, and Carrie.

The little log house stood far away from the next neighbor and even farther away from a town.

Like every family that lived in the wild country in those days, Laura's family had to make, grow, or find almost everything they needed. Pa cut trees into big logs for the house and barn and small logs for the fire. He trapped wild animals for furs, which could be sold for things the family could not make or grow.

Ma made the clothes and did the cooking. She helped take care of the garden and sometimes milked the cow, Sukey.

Everyone in the family had little jobs, or chores, to do. Even little Laura helped Ma set the table and feed the animals.

Life in the big woods was hard. But it was not all work. Like most little girls, Laura, Mary, and Carrie had their dolls. On warm days they played outside. At night Pa told them stories, and they all sang together by the fire.

Living in the big woods was sometimes exciting and even dangerous. Wild animals were never far away. And during the long snowy winter, weeks might go by without the family seeing any other people.

The story that you are about to read began on a spring day, when Laura was five years old. That morning Pa had gone to the town to sell the furs and get things for the family. Ma and the girls had stayed home to take care of the chores. At last it was sundown, and Pa had not yet returned.

PART ONE

The Big Bear

The sun sank out of sight, the woods grew dark, and he did not come. Ma started supper and set the table, but he did not come. It was time to do the chores, and still he had not come.

Ma said that Laura might come with her while she milked the cow. Laura could carry the lantern.

So Laura put on her coat and Ma buttoned it up. And Laura put her hands into her red mittens that hung by a red yarn string around her neck, while Ma lighted the candle in the lantern.

Laura was proud to be helping Ma with the milking, and she carried the lantern very carefully. Its sides were of tin, with places cut in them for the candle-light to shine through.

When Laura walked behind Ma on the path to the barn, the little bits of candle-light from the lantern leaped all around her on the snow. The night was not yet quite dark. The woods were dark, but there was a gray light on the snowy path, and in the sky there were a few faint stars. The stars did not look as warm and bright as the little lights that came from the lantern.

Laura was surprised to see the dark shape of Sukey, the brown cow, standing at the barnyard gate. Ma was surprised, too.

It was too early in the spring for Sukey to be let out in the Big Woods to eat grass. She lived in the barn. But sometimes on warm days Pa left the door of her stall open so she could come into the barnyard. Now Ma and Laura saw her behind the bars, waiting for them.

Ma went up to the gate, and pushed against it to open it. But it did not open very far, because there was Sukey, standing against it.

Ma said, "Sukey, get over!" She reached across the gate and slapped Sukey's shoulder.

Just then one of the dancing little bits of light from the lantern jumped between the bars of the gate, and Laura saw long, shaggy, black fur, and two little, glittering eyes.

Sukey had thin, short, brown fur. Sukey had large, gentle eyes.

Ma said, "Laura, walk back to the house."

So Laura turned around and began to walk toward the house. Ma came behind her. When they had gone part way, Ma snatched her up, lantern and all, and ran. Ma ran with her into the house, and slammed the door.

Then Laura said, "Ma, was it a bear?"

"Yes, Laura," Ma said. "It was a bear."

Laura began to cry. She hung on to Ma and sobbed, "Oh, will he eat Sukey?"

"No," Ma said, hugging her. "Sukey is safe in the barn. Think, Laura—all those big, heavy logs in the barn walls. And the door is heavy and solid, made to keep bears out. No, the bear cannot get in and eat Sukey."

Laura felt better then. "But he could have hurt us, couldn't he?" she asked.

"He didn't hurt us," Ma said. "You were a good girl, Laura, to do exactly as I told you, and to do it quickly, without asking why."

Ma was trembling, and she began to laugh a little. "To think," she said, "I've slapped a bear!"

Then she put supper on the table for Laura and Mary. Pa had not come yet. He didn't come. Laura and Mary were undressed, and they said their prayers and snuggled into the trundle bed.

Ma sat by the lamp, mending one of Pa's shirts. The house seemed cold and still and strange, without Pa.

Laura listened to the wind in the Big Woods. All around the house the wind went crying as though it were lost in the dark and the cold. The wind sounded frightened.

Ma finished mending the shirt. Laura saw her fold it slowly and carefully. She smoothed it with her hand. Then she did a thing she had never done before. She went to the door and pulled the leather latch-string through its hole in the door, so that nobody could get in from outside unless she lifted the latch. She came and took Carrie, all limp and sleeping, out of the big bed.

She saw that Laura and Mary were still awake, and she said to them: "Go to sleep, girls. Everything is all right. Pa will be here in the morning."

Then she went back to her rocking chair and sat there rocking gently and holding Baby Carrie in her arms.

She was sitting up late, waiting for Pa, and Laura and Mary meant to stay awake, too, till he came. But at last they went to sleep.

In the morning Pa was there. He had brought candy for Laura and Mary, and two pieces of pretty calico to make them each a dress. Mary's was a china-blue pattern on a white ground, and Laura's was dark red with little golden-brown dots on it. Ma had calico for a dress, too; it was brown, with a big, feathery white pattern all over it.

They were all happy because Pa had got such good prices for his furs that he could afford to get them such beautiful presents.

The tracks of the big bear were all around the barn, and there were marks of his claws on the walls. But Sukey and the horses were safe inside.

All that day the sun shone, the snow melted, and little streams of water ran from the icicles, which all the time grew thinner. Before the sun set that night, the bear tracks were only shapeless marks in the wet, soft snow.

After supper Pa took Laura and Mary on his knees and said he had a new story to tell them.

PART TWO

Pa and the Bear in the Way

"When I went to town yesterday with the furs, I found it hard walking in the soft snow. It took me a long time to get to town, and other men with furs had come in earlier to do their trading. The storekeeper was busy, and I had to wait until he could look at my furs.

"Then we had to bargain about the price of each one, and then I had to pick out the things I wanted to take in trade.

"So it was nearly sundown before I could start home.

"I tried to hurry, but the walking was hard and I was tired, so I had not gone far before night came. And I was alone in the Big Woods without my gun."

"There were still six miles to walk, and I came along as fast as I could. The night grew darker and darker, and I wished for my gun, because I knew that some of the bears had come out of their winter dens. I had seen their tracks when I went to town in the morning.

"Bears are hungry and cross at this time of year; you know they have been sleeping in their dens all winter long with nothing to eat, and that makes them thin and angry when they wake up. I did not want to meet one.

"I hurried along as quick as I could in the dark. By and by the stars gave a little light. It was still black as pitch where the woods were thick, but in the open places I could see, dimly. I could see the snowy road ahead a little way, and I could see the dark woods standing all around me. I was glad when I came into an open place where the stars gave me this faint light.

"All the time I was watching, as well as I could, for bears. I was listening for the sounds they make when they go carelessly through the bushes.

"Then I came again into an open place, and there, right in the middle of my road, I saw a big black bear.

"He was standing up on his hind legs, looking at me. I could see his eyes shine. I could see his pig-snout. I could even see one of his claws, in the starlight.

"My scalp prickled, and my hair stood straight up. I stopped in my tracks, and stood still. The bear did not move. There he stood, looking at me.

"I knew it would do no good to try to go around him. He would follow me into the dark woods, where he could see better than I could. I did not want to fight a winter-starved bear in the dark. Oh, how I wished for my gun!

"I had to pass that bear, to get home. I thought that if I could scare him, he might get out of the road and let me go by. So I took a deep breath, and suddenly I shouted with all my might and ran at him, waving my arms.

"He didn't move.

"I did not run very far toward him, I tell you!

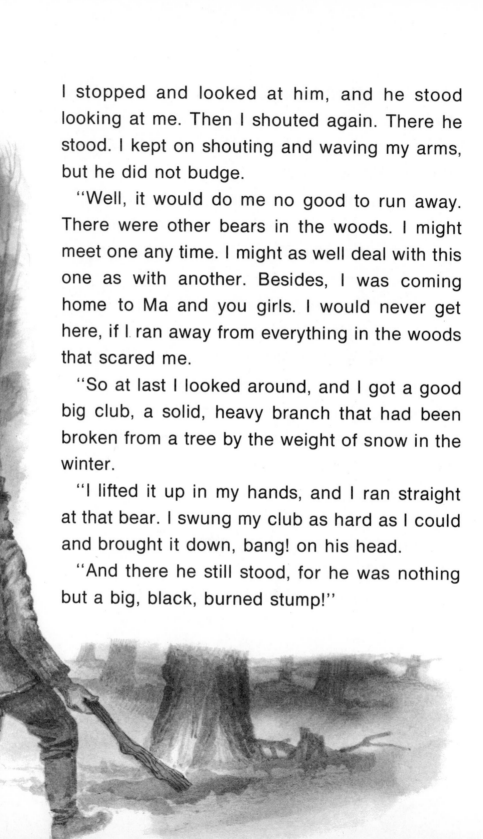

I stopped and looked at him, and he stood looking at me. Then I shouted again. There he stood. I kept on shouting and waving my arms, but he did not budge.

"Well, it would do me no good to run away. There were other bears in the woods. I might meet one any time. I might as well deal with this one as with another. Besides, I was coming home to Ma and you girls. I would never get here, if I ran away from everything in the woods that scared me.

"So at last I looked around, and I got a good big club, a solid, heavy branch that had been broken from a tree by the weight of snow in the winter.

"I lifted it up in my hands, and I ran straight at that bear. I swung my club as hard as I could and brought it down, bang! on his head.

"And there he still stood, for he was nothing but a big, black, burned stump!"

"I had passed it on my way to town that morning. It wasn't a bear at all. I only thought it was a bear, because I had been thinking all the time about bears and being afraid I'd meet one."

"It really wasn't a bear at all?" Mary asked.

"No, Mary, it wasn't a bear at all. There I had been yelling, and dancing, and waving my arms, all by myself in the Big Woods, trying to scare a stump!"

Laura said: "Ours was really a bear. But we were not scared, because we thought it was Sukey."

Pa did not say anything, but he hugged her tighter.

"Oo-oo! That bear might have eaten Ma and me all up!" Laura said, snuggling closer to him. "But Ma walked right up to him and slapped him, and he didn't do anything at all. Why didn't he do anything?"

"I guess he was too surprised to do anything, Laura," Pa said. "I guess he was afraid, when the lantern shone in his eyes. And when Ma walked up to him and slapped him, he knew *she* wasn't afraid."

"Well, you were brave, too," Laura said. "Even if it was only a stump, you thought it was a bear. You'd have hit him on the head with a club, if he *had* been a bear, wouldn't you, Pa?"

"Yes," said Pa, "I would. You see, I had to."

Old Log House

On a little green knoll
At the edge of the wood,
My great-great-grandmother's
First house stood.

The house was of logs
My grandmother said,
With one big room
And a lean-to-shed.

I like to hear
My grandmother tell
How they built the fireplace
And dug the well.

Forever and ever
I wish I could
Live in a house
At the edge of a wood.

—James S. Tippett

3 NEVER GIVE UP!

A single flower
Pushed right through
A sidewalk crack
So hopeful and strong.

—*Hannah Lyons Johnson*

185

The Case of the
Silver
Fruit Bowl

Donald J. Sobol

"Stay away from Idaville!"

Across the country, crooks, big and small, soon got the word. They knew what would happen if they tried anything funny in Idaville — a quick trip to jail. For more than a year, no man, woman, or child had broken a law in Idaville and gotten away with it.

How did Idaville do it? How did it win its war on crime? No one could guess. Idaville looked like any other small town near the sea. It had a park, a library, a bank, a lovely beach, and good places to fish.

And on Spring Street, it had a red house with a garden around it. This was the real headquarters of Idaville's war on crime. For within those red walls lived Encyclopedia Brown.

Encyclopedia's father was chief of the Idaville police. For more than a year now, Chief Brown had been bringing home his hardest cases. Encyclopedia solved them at the dinner table.

Chief Brown wanted to tell the world that his son was a great detective. He wanted to shout,

"My son is the greatest detective who ever walked in sneakers!"

But how could he? Who would believe that the brain behind Idaville's crime cleanup was only ten years old?

Encyclopedia never said a word about the help he gave his father. He didn't want to seem different from any other ten-year-old.

The name Encyclopedia was something else. There was nothing he could do about it. Only his mother, father, and teacher called him by his real name, Leroy. Everyone else called him Encyclopedia.

An encyclopedia is a book or set of books filled with facts from A to Z. So was Encyclopedia's head. You might say he was the only library in the country that could play first base.

One night at dinner, his father ate his soup very slowly. At once, Encyclopedia knew why. Chief Brown had come across a hard case.

Chief Brown put down his spoon. He sat back and said, "Mr. Herman, the owner of the Silver Shop, says he was held up this afternoon."

"*Says?*" Mrs. Brown asked. "You make it sound as if you don't believe him."

"I'm not sure," said Chief Brown. "He says that eight silver dishes were stolen. But no one saw the holdup."

"Why should he be lying?" asked Mrs. Brown.

"Mr. Herman doesn't own the dishes that were stolen. He would not have lost any money because of the holdup," said Chief Brown. "The dishes are Mrs. Edwards'. Mr. Herman was going to try to sell them for her. If he sold them, Mrs. Edwards was to pay him for his time and trouble."

"Do you think he said the dishes were stolen so that he could sell them out of town and keep all the money?" asked Encyclopedia.

"It has been done before, Leroy," said Chief Brown.

"Did Mr. Herman see who held him up?" asked Mrs. Brown.

"One man," said Chief Brown. "Mr. Herman is sure he will know the man if he sees him again."

Chief Brown reached into his shirt pocket and took out a notebook. "I wrote down everything Mr. Herman told me about the holdup," he said. Then he read from his notebook.

"I was alone in the store just after one o'clock. I had my back to the door. I was locking a wall case in which I keep eight fine silver dishes belonging to Mrs. Edwards. I heard the door open. A man's voice said, 'Don't turn around—this is a holdup!' I felt a gun in my back. 'Just hand over everything in the case,' the voice said. After I had given him everything, he left."

Encyclopedia said, "If Mr. Herman had his back to the holdup man all the time, how would he know the man if he saw him again?"

Mrs. Brown looked proudly at Encyclopedia. She was always pleased when he solved a case so quickly.

"Mr. Herman said something else," said Chief Brown. He read again from his notebook.

"The dishes were very shiny. Before I handed over the fruit bowl, I looked inside. I saw the man's face just as if I were looking into a mirror."

Chief Brown put his notebook into his pocket. "You see," he said, "I can't be sure that Mr. Herman is lying."

"Is his store doing well?" asked Encyclopedia.

"No," said Chief Brown. "I called his bank. He has borrowed a lot of money. I think he made up that story about the holdup. With the money he will get from selling the silver out of town, he can give back the money he borrowed."

"You're not being fair," said Mrs. Brown. "Just because Mr. Herman needs money doesn't mean he stole Mrs. Edwards' silver."

"Have you ever seen the shiny silver bowl he used as a mirror, Dad?" asked Encyclopedia.

"Your mother and I nearly bought the bowl last week, as a matter of fact," said Chief Brown. "It's about a foot across and rounded inside like a big spoon."

"We just loved it," said Mrs. Brown. "But we didn't want to spend that much money on a silver bowl."

"I'm happy you didn't," said Encyclopedia.

"Why?" asked Chief Brown.

"Mr. Herman needed the fruit bowl for his story," said Encyclopedia. "He had to say something that showed he acted to get back the silver dishes. So he put in the part about using the fruit bowl as a mirror to see the holdup man's face."

"I'm afraid that part doesn't matter, Leroy," said Chief Brown. "We don't know for sure that he didn't see the man any more than we can know for sure that he made up the rest of the story. We're back where we started."

"Not quite, Dad," said Encyclopedia. "We know that Mr. Herman is lying!"

ARE YOU A GOOD DETECTIVE? WHAT MADE ENCYCLOPEDIA SURE?

To see how Encyclopedia solved his case,

turn to page 323.

Dina Anastasio

Mary of Valley Forge

The English were among the first people to bring their families from Europe to live in America. They cut down the forests and used the logs from the trees to build houses. English ships brought many things they needed to live in the woods. English soldiers stayed to help guard the people.

At first these new families were happy to have help from England. But as the years went by, their feelings toward England began to change.

A time came when most of the people living
in America wanted their own country.
In 1775 America went to war with England
to win the right to be a free country.

George Washington became the head of the
first American Army. For a few years the new
American Army lost more battles than it won.
But then things began to change. Many
people believe the change came in 1778.
General Washington and his men had spent
that winter at a place called Valley Forge.

For the American Army, it was the hardest
winter of the war. Heavy snow kept wagons
from bringing in food. Many soldiers became
sick from cold and hunger.

Many people helped the American Army
get through that long winter at Valley Forge.
One of them was a young girl named Mary
McDonald. This is her story.

Winter at Valley Forge

One dark snowy morning in the winter of 1778, Mary left her home. She set out with a basket of apples and nuts for Valley Forge.

Mary could not remember such a winter. There had been nothing but snowstorms. The rivers were solid ice. Because of snow and English soldiers, the roads to Valley Forge had been closed.

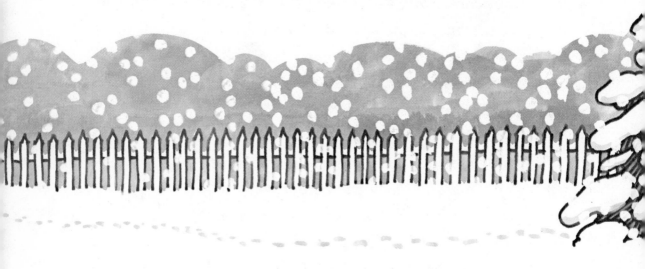

For a long time, there had been no meat, fish, or bread for the soldiers at Valley Forge. The Army was sick and hungry. It might not last until spring.

Slowly Mary made her way through the deep snow that covered the parade ground. She tramped by the small log houses, where many American soldiers lay sick, cold, and hungry.

At last she came to a large stone house. It was the headquarters of General George Washington. A tall soldier stood watch at the door. Mary stood by a tree near the house and watched him. His coat was torn and thin.

The soldier saw something move and called out,

"Who goes there?"

Mary was afraid. But she walked over to him and whispered, "May I see General Washington?"

The soldier looked surprised. He asked, "Why do you want to see General Washington?"

Mary could hardly talk. In a small voice she said, "I'd like to join the army."

"Wait here," the soldier said, and he went into the house.

Mary put her cold hands deep into the pockets of her coat and waited. Soon the soldier returned and told her to come with him. He led her inside to a small sitting room, where some women were working and talking. A short woman with white hair got up as they came in. She looked down at Mary and smiled.

"I'm told you'd like to join our army," she said.

"Yes," Mary whispered. She was still very afraid.

"How old are you?" the woman asked.

"Almost eight."

"And your name?"

"Mary McDonald."

"Well then, Mary," the woman said, "I'm Mrs. Washington. These women and I are filling baskets with food. When the baskets have been filled, they will be taken to the soldiers."

Mrs. Washington looked at Mary carefully and said, "Maybe you can help. Would you like to take the food to the men?"

"Oh, yes. I would like that," Mary said. "I've brought some food, too." She put the basket of nuts and apples on the table.

"Wonderful," a deep voice from the doorway said. Mary turned quickly. A tall, very handsome man in a blue coat stood in the doorway.

"Mary," Mrs. Washington said, leading her toward the door. "This is General Washington."

To General Washington she said, "Mary's going to help carry food to the soldiers."

The General smiled. "That's fine," he said. He took Mary to the window, and together they looked out at the snow-covered log houses.

"Many of the men are sick from hunger, Mary," the General told her. "You will be helping them very much."

As they stood by the window, the General started to talk, more to himself than to Mary. "I wonder if spring will ever come," he said. "We can't beat the English without food." Then, with head down, he left the room.

"I belong to the first American Army," Mary thought. "And it is going to be the best army in the whole world."

Spring at Valley Forge

The next morning Mary pulled her coat around her and set out for the stone house. The same tall soldier stood guard by the front door. But this time when he saw her, he smiled.

"Mrs. Washington is waiting for you," he said. Mary ran through the small dark hall and up the stairs. She stood silently by the sitting room door and watched the women as they worked. She thought they looked very beautiful.

"Come in, child," Mrs. Washington said.

Mary walked into the room. She put the food which she had brought from home on the table. Then she sat down and waited while the women filled the baskets. Some of their husbands had been hurt in the battles of the past year. Many more of them were very sick from cold and hunger. But when the women talked of spring, there was hope in their voices. The roads would be opened again. They could get the food their husbands needed to become strong again.

When the women had filled their baskets, Mrs. Washington stood and smiled at Mary.

"Now, Mary," she said, giving her two baskets, "take this food to the soldiers."

Mary carried the baskets down the stairs and past the tall soldier, who again smiled at her. She tramped through the deep snow and passed the building where General Washington's gray horse stood waiting. She passed another building where flour and water cakes were baking.

The wind was cold, and the baskets were heavy. But Mary was proud to be part of the American Army. At last she came to a row of log huts and opened the first door.

Mary saw the soldiers lying silently on their beds. A small fire burned in the fireplace at the far end of the log hut. But the room was cold and dark.

Mary walked quietly to the first bed and looked down at the sleeping soldier. The man looked very weak.

"I've brought you some food," Mary whispered.

"So you've brought food," the soldier said in a weak voice. "That's a nice surprise. What's your name?"

"Mary," she answered.

The soldier smiled and said, "Well, Mary, I'm Tom, and I sure can use some food."

Mary gave him some fruit and nuts. He ate quickly while Mary watched. When Tom had finished he said, "That was better than the flour and water cakes we've been living on.

"More snow I see," Tom said sadly, looking at Mary's coat. "Every night I dream that the snow has melted, and the roads have been cleared. I dream that wagons are pulling food through again. And every day I look outside and see snow and more snow."

"Don't worry, Tom," Mary said. "Spring will come. It always does." She touched his hand and moved on. Other soldiers had been waiting silently for food.

Mary gave each soldier some nuts and a little fruit. The men shook her hand and thanked her.

All day long Mary walked through the deep snow carrying baskets of food from General Washington's headquarters to the men in the log huts.

During the next two months, Mary walked many miles carrying baskets from the stone house to the huts. The soldiers looked ahead with pleasure to her visit.

Tuesday was a special day for Mary because that was the day she took food to the hut where Tom lived. Tom had become her special friend. She wished that she could bring him food every day.

One Tuesday after breakfast, Mary put on her coat and started out for Valley Forge. The deep snow was shimmering in the sunlight. Suddenly Mary noticed that the snow was melting. She took off her coat. Yet, she still felt quite warm.

"*Spring is coming!*" she shouted, as she ran past the guard at the stone house. The guard laughed.

Mrs. Washington and the other women were standing by the window when Mary came into the sitting room. They, too, had seen the melting snow. Mary thought they looked really happy for the first time since she had been coming to Valley Forge.

Mary picked up the baskets and hurried through the melting snow to the hut where Tom lived.

"*Spring is here,*" she shouted as she opened the door. Some of the men got up from their beds and walked weakly to the door. When they saw the melting snow and felt the warm air, they shouted with joy.

Tom did not get up. He lay very weak and quiet on his bed. Mary went over to him.

"Please come to the door, Tom," she said. "You will feel better."

Slowly, Tom got up and walked to the door.

"Now you will get better," Mary said.

When Tom felt the warm air and saw the melting snow, he smiled happily and said, "Yes, I know."

Spring brought life and hope to Valley Forge. After the roads had been cleared, wagons came bringing meat and other things the men needed.

When the men were strong enough, they went to the parade ground to drill. For two months, day after day they went there. At last the men were ready for battle again.

One fine day in June, the soldiers marched out of Valley Forge to meet the English. On that day in June, Mary stood on a small hill near the river and watched them pass. Their clothes were torn and thin, but they held their heads proudly as they marched to the music of the beating drums. Some of them saw Mary and waved at her.

At last, Mary saw Tom. His clothes were old. He had no shoes. But he was no longer sick and hungry. When he saw her, he waved. Then he turned and marched off to fight the war.

After the Americans had won the war, they elected George Washington the first President of their new country. President Washington never forgot the winter that his brave army spent at Valley Forge. And Mary was always proud to have been part of it. She never forgot that she had once met our first President.

George Washington's Breakfast

Jean Fritz

PART ONE

George W. Allen

George W. Allen was proud of two things—his name and his birthday. George was named for George Washington, and he had the same birthday. It made him want to know everything about George Washington. And he knew a lot.

Then one day George W. Allen thought of something he didn't know. George's mother and father had gone off to work. His grandmother was cooking eggs.

"Grandma," George said, "what did George Washington eat for breakfast?"

"How should I know?" said his grandmother. "That was before my time. And don't think that I'm going to help you find out, either!"

George's grandmother knew what George was like. Whenever he wanted to find out something, he just couldn't rest until he did. He didn't let anyone else rest either. George did just what his grandfather used to do—ask questions, collect books, and pester everyone for answers. George's grandmother wasn't going to fool around now about breakfasts that were over and done with so many years ago.

"Well," George said, "if I find out, will you cook me George Washington's breakfast?"

George's grandmother looked at the clock on the wall. "George, you'll be late for school," she said.

"But will you?" George asked. "Will you cook me George Washington's breakfast?"

George's grandmother was still looking at the clock.

"I'll cook anything," she said, "if you hurry."

After school that day George went right to the library. Miss Willing, the woman in charge, smiled when she saw George come in. "I wonder what that Allen boy wants to know now," she thought.

"Miss Willing," said George, "do you know what George Washington ate for breakfast?"

Miss Willing could hardly remember what she'd had for breakfast that morning. But like George, she liked to find out answers.

Together George and Miss Willing went to the encyclopedia and looked under *W.* "Washington, George." The encyclopedia said that he was born in 1732, married in 1759, was elected President in 1789, and died in 1799. It told about his trips and the battles he fought. But it didn't say what he ate for breakfast.

Miss Willing showed George where to find the books about George Washington. George picked out four of them to take home. Miss Willing promised that she would read some of the rest.

That night after supper, George gave his father and mother each a book to read.

"Don't look at me," his grandmother said. "I said I'd cook, but I won't look."

So George kept the other two books for himself. But not one of the books said anything about what George Washington ate for breakfast.

Day after day George, his mother and father, and Miss Willing read. Then one day Miss Willing said they had read all the books about Washington.

Then George had a good idea. "Let's go to Washington's home in Mount Vernon where his breakfasts were cooked."

The next weekend George and Mr. and Mrs. Allen got into the car and started out for Mount Vernon. It was a long trip. When they got there, George and his mother and father went right to the kitchen. They walked on the same path that Washington had walked on. Every time George Allen put his feet down, he thought of George Washington's feet in the same place.

The kitchen was at the side of the house. It was a large room with a big fireplace at one end and lots of pots and pans at the other. George held his breath. It was at that very fireplace that Washington's breakfasts had been cooked.

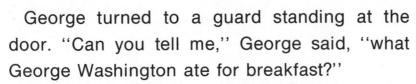

George turned to a guard standing at the door. "Can you tell me," George said, "what George Washington ate for breakfast?"

The guard answered, "Breakfast was at 7:00. People were given cold meats and tea."

"And did George Washington eat the same breakfast?" George asked.

"I don't know," said the guard. "I've only been here eight weeks."

On Sunday George and his mother and father went home. George's grandmother and Miss Willing were waiting for them.

"No luck," George said to them.

"It was a good try, son. You can't win them all," said Mrs. Allen.

Mr. Allen put his hand on George's shoulder. "Sometimes there's nothing to do but give up," Mr. Allen said.

"Give up?"

"I can't give up!" George shouted. "George Washington's men didn't have enough to eat during the war, and they didn't give up. What do you think I am?"

George was so mad, he went up to the attic and closed the door. It was quiet up there.

PART TWO

The Book in the Attic

In the attic was a box filled with things George guessed his grandmother was going to throw away. On top of the box was an old stuffed dog. He remembered that dog. His name was Homer. One ear was ripped now. George put him aside.

George looked back in the box and saw some old comics. It was a good thing he'd come up here, he thought. No one should throw away old comics. Under the comics George found a very old book. It must have been his grandfather's.

He found a part on George Washington and began to read. "Washington breakfasts about 7:00 on . . ." George let out a yell, took the book, and ran out of the attic.

"Grandma!" he shouted. "George Washington breakfasts about 7:00 on three small Indian hoecakes and tea!"

"George," said his grandmother. "I don't have any idea what an Indian hoecake is."

George went to the dictionary. He looked under *H*. "Hoecake. A cake of cornmeal and water and salt baked before an open fire on a hoe."

"I've cornmeal and water and salt," said Grandma. "I guess I can make some Indian hoecakes."

George's father made a fire in the fireplace, and George's mother filled the kettle with water for the tea.

George said he was going to look for a hoe, but his grandmother stopped him. "You don't want me to cook those things on a hoe, do you?" she asked.

"Well, that's what the dictionary says," said George.

George's grandmother looked in the dictionary. "The dictionary means that a hoe was used when hoecakes were first made. I think hoecakes were around a long time before Washington. Did you see a hoe in George Washington's kitchen in Mount Vernon?" she asked.

George said he hadn't seen one.

"Then we'll use what we have," said Grandma. She mixed the cornmeal and water and salt in a bowl and then made little cakes.

Soon the tea kettle began to steam and the hoecakes began to turn a nice golden brown.

George Washington's breakfast was ready at last.

George took a bite of hoecake. It was pretty good, he thought. He looked at his mother and father and his grandmother and Miss Willing all eating hoecakes together on a Sunday afternoon. George felt closer to Washington than he'd ever felt in his whole life. It was as if George Washington were there at the fireplace with them.

But when George finished his three small hoecakes and his tea, he was still hungry. And if he was hungry, what about Washington? For a man who was six feet tall and the Father of His Country, it wasn't much of a breakfast.

"I hope Washington didn't have long to wait for lunch," George said. "I hope he had a nice big lunch waiting for him. I wonder what . . ."

"George Washington Allen," his grandmother cried. "Don't you say another word."

"Not today," Miss Willing said. "The library is closed today."

"Okay," said George. "Not today."

Look It Up!

Sue, Bill, Jack, and Mary are all looking for facts about cornmeal. Sue is looking in a dictionary. Bill is looking in an encyclopedia. Jack is looking in a cookbook. Mary is looking in the glossary in *Never Give Up!*

Who is trying to find out what part of speech *cornmeal* is?

Who is trying to find out what *cornmeal* means in "George Washington's Breakfast"?

Who is trying to find out how much cornmeal to use in making hoecakes?

Who is trying to find out how much cornmeal is made in the United States each year?

in People Sports

All these people have worked very hard to become great sports stars. All of them are champions!

TRACY AUSTIN

Tracy Austin has been playing tennis since she was three years old. She has become one of the world's best tennis players. For Tracy Austin, 1977 was a year to remember. At 14 years of age, she became the youngest player to compete at Wimbledon, England—one of the most famous tournaments in the world.

HANK AARON

On April 8, 1974, forty-year-old Hank Aaron set a new world record in baseball. He hit the 715th home run of his long career, beating the record set by Babe Ruth many years ago. Hank Aaron has been a great ballplayer for a long time. But nothing in his long career has topped that famous home run.

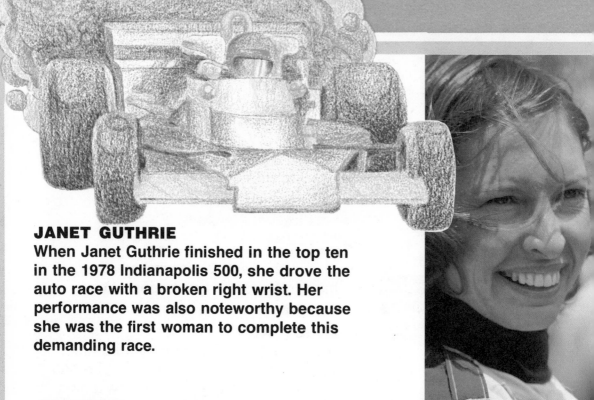

JANET GUTHRIE

When Janet Guthrie finished in the top ten in the 1978 Indianapolis 500, she drove the auto race with a broken right wrist. Her performance was also noteworthy because she was the first woman to complete this demanding race.

LEE TREVINO

Lee Trevino was only six years old when he taught himself to play golf. He used apples for golf balls and an old club that had been cut off to match his small size. He practiced every day on a homemade golf course with only two holes.

All the hard work finally paid off! When Lee Trevino won the Colonial National in 1978, it marked the eleventh consecutive year he had won a Professional Golfers' Association tournament. During this period he won the United States Open twice.

MARGARET WADE

Because of Margaret Wade's outstanding achievement as a basketball player and coach, an award was created in her honor in 1978. The Wade Trophy is presented annually to the nation's best female college basketball player. At that point in her career, Margaret Wade had coached Delta State University, in Mississippi, to three national women's basketball titles.

CAROL BLAZEJOWSKI

In 1978, Carol Blazejowski was the first winner of the Wade Trophy. "Blaze" led Montclair State College, in New Jersey, to a third-place finish in the national tournament that year. She scored 40 or more points in each of her last three games, to finish the year with 3,119 career points, second highest in the all-time college ranks.

Would you like to be a sports star some day? Would you work hard to become one?

NEVER GIVE UP!
Special Olympics

"Let me win, but if I cannot,
let me be brave in the attempt."

The children who take part in the
Special Olympics not only recite this
oath, they also live by it. They remind
us of the true meaning of character,
courage, and competition.

The Special Olympics is the largest program of sports training and athletic competition for the mentally retarded in the world. Since the Joseph P. Kennedy, Jr., Foundation created it in 1968, it has become a year-round program in every state and some foreign countries. It gives the special child the chance to share in the joyful experiences that are so important for all children.

Where the Good Luck Was

Osmond Molarsky

PART ONE

The Crutches

On Sunday Agnes got out of the hospital. Her three best friends were sitting on her front stairs. They were waiting for her to come home.

"How come you have crutches?" Jack said. "We thought you were well."

"I have to walk on crutches for three months," Agnes said. "I broke my leg."

"Next time I bet you won't jump off a roof," Ruth said. "Even with an umbrella!"

"How come you have those old wooden crutches?" Kevin asked. "You should have aluminum crutches."

"They cost twenty-four dollars and fifty cents," Agnes said. "The hospital lent me these wooden crutches. But I don't need them. Watch this." Agnes swung her feet up in front, then up in back. She galloped off to the corner and back. "I've got the fastest crutches in the West," she said. "Who wants to race me?"

None of her friends wanted to race her. They were thinking.

Then Kevin said, "Agnes should have some shiny aluminum crutches. A kid on our block with aluminum crutches! That would be cool!"

"How would you like that, Agnes?" Jack asked.

"That's okay with me," Agnes said.

"Let's start an Agnes McWilliams Aluminum Crutches Fund and get her some," said Kevin.

"How do we get the money?" Ruth asked.

"Easy," Jack said. But he wasn't really sure.

Just then Lucky came tearing around the corner, carrying a long stick. Lucky was always finding things. Once, a long time ago, she found a new pocket knife. After that, she always walked with her head down, so she wouldn't miss anything on the ground. But now she was running, not walking. She held her head high.

"What's up, Lucky?" said Jack.

"Who's got some gum?" Lucky asked. Lucky was excited. "You know the sidewalk grating in front of the toy store? I saw a quarter down there!" she said. "With some gum on the end of this stick, I could get it. Who has some gum?"

Jack said, "I have a piece in my pocket. For three cents, I'll let you use it."

"Three cents!" Lucky said. "For ten cents I could get a whole pack!"

"Wait," said Kevin. 'We're starting a fund to buy Agnes aluminum crutches. What if Jack gives the gum to Lucky, and Lucky gives the quarter to the fund?"

"Why can't Agnes use wooden crutches?" Lucky asked.

"A kid on our block with real aluminum crutches would be cool," said Jack.

Lucky tried to think why Agnes shouldn't have aluminum crutches. "Okay," she said at last. "I'll give the quarter. But Jack gives me the gum."

"You know what?" said Kevin. "I bet there are fifty gratings around here. We could get money for the fund from all of them."

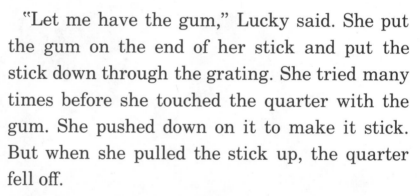

"Let me have the gum," Lucky said. She put the gum on the end of her stick and put the stick down through the grating. She tried many times before she touched the quarter with the gum. She pushed down on it to make it stick. But when she pulled the stick up, the quarter fell off.

"I've got an idea," said Kevin. "Ruth, give me your magnet." Ruth handed her magnet to Kevin. "Who's got some string?" Kevin asked.

"Here," said Jack, and in a minute Kevin was letting the magnet down on the end of the string. At last the magnet touched the quarter. Kevin began to pull the magnet up. Nothing was on it but an old nail that had been next to the quarter.

"Are we silly!" Kevin said. "I just remembered. A magnet picks up iron and steel. A quarter isn't made of iron or steel."

"There has got to be a way to get money out of gratings," Lucky said.

Just then Mr. M. B. Pendleton walked by the children. "What are you doing?" he asked.

"We are trying to get that quarter up from the grating," Lucky said. "But it won't work."

"A quarter?" said the old man.

"We need it to buy aluminum crutches for Agnes. She has a broken leg," said Kevin.

"How would you like to make some money for the crutches?" asked Mr. Pendleton.

"We would like that," said Ruth. "But how?"

"My attic is full of junk I want to throw away—old newspapers, old clothes, old books," said the old man. "I'll pay you kids fifty cents an hour to carry it out to the sidewalk for the garbage pickup."

"Does each of us get fifty cents an hour?" Jack wanted to know. "Or is that for all of us?"

"Fifty cents an hour for all of you," the old man said.

"Wait a minute," said Jack, and he got all his friends together. They whispered for a minute. Then he said, "We want twenty cents an hour for each of us."

"All right," said Mr. Pendleton. "Come with me."

"I'm staying here to get that quarter," said Lucky.

"Good luck, Lucky," said Kevin, and off the children went with Mr. Pendleton.

PART TWO

The Leather Box

The houses on the old man's block were big and tall. But the biggest of all was the house of Mr. M. B. Pendleton. The children had seen it. but they had never been inside it.

"Here we are," said the old man. He took out his big key ring and let them into the house. He led them up to the attic.

All over the attic were old tables, lamps, and piles of newspapers. There were boxes with writing on them that said *Books, Mary's Wedding Dress, Peter's Football.* There was even a small box marked *Rags.* Kevin picked it up and thought it was very heavy for a box of rags.

The children went up and down the stairs like ants, carrying bundles and putting them on the sidewalk. In less than three hours, the job was done.

"That makes me feel much better. How much do I owe you?" asked Mr. Pendleton.

"We started at one o'clock," Jack said. "Now it's five minutes to four."

"Let's call it three hours," the old gentleman said. "At twenty cents an hour for three of you, that's sixty cents for each hour. Three hours is a dollar and eighty cents. I'll make it two dollars even." He gave the children the money.

"Now all we need is twenty-two dollars and fifty cents more," Jack said.

"Listen," said Kevin. "Remember how heavy that little box was that was marked *Rags*?"

"Yes," said Jack.

"I'm going to look inside it," Kevin said. The children watched as Kevin opened the box.

"Those are rags, all right," Jack said.

"Rags can't be that heavy," Kevin said. He reached in and pulled out some rags. Under them was a leather box. Kevin lifted the lid.

"It's nothing but some old silver," said Kevin.

"I thought it might be worth something," said Ruth.

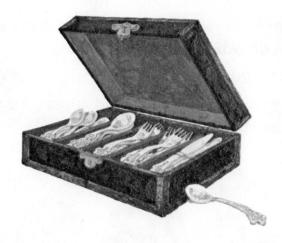

Kevin lifted out a silver spoon. It was a beautiful shape. "Maybe if we shine the silver, it might be worth a lot of money," he said. "We could sell it."

"We can't sell it. It belongs to Mr. Pendleton," Ruth said.

"He told us to take it away," said Kevin. "It's just like we found it. Finders, keepers! The garbage truck would have come and taken the box."

"I think we should tell Mr. Pendleton," Ruth said.

Kevin picked up the black box, and the boys went up the steps and knocked on the door.

Mr. Pendleton opened the door. "Yes?" he said.

Kevin showed him the box. The old man looked at the silver. "This belonged to my grandmother," he said.

"Did you mean to throw it away?" Jack asked. "It was in a box that said *Rags*. We put the box out with the rest of the stuff."

"Well," Mr. Pendleton said, "you have done me a very good turn. This silver is worth a lot to me. You should have something in return. What do you think it should be?"

Suddenly a thought came to Jack. "Twenty-two dollars and fifty cents," he said.

"If that is what you want, that is what you will get," said Mr. Pendleton. He took out his billfold and gave them exactly twenty-two dollars and fifty cents.

The children thanked Mr. Pendleton and hurried to find Agnes. Then, with Agnes, they went to the store to get the new crutches.

Inside the store, Jack said to the clerk, "We'd like to look at some aluminum crutches. They're for her," and he looked at Agnes.

"Yes," said the clerk, and he brought out some crutches. "There you are! Try them."

Agnes walked up and down. "They are nice and light," she said. Then she swung her feet up in the air. She sat down hard. Her friends picked her up. "That hurt," she said.

"What did you think you were doing?" said the clerk. "Crutches are not to do tricks on."

"Aluminum ones aren't. I can see that," said Agnes. "I'll stick to wooden crutches."

Everyone was disappointed. No child on their block would have aluminum crutches. And what would they do with the twenty-four dollars and fifty cents in the Agnes McWilliams Aluminum Crutches Fund?

Agnes could see that her friends were disappointed. She tried to think how she could make it up to them. "Remember the hospital lent me these crutches until I get well," she said. "I've got an idea. They have plenty of crutches but no aluminum ones."

"I get it," said Ruth. "We can give the aluminum crutches to the hospital."

"Right," said Agnes. "Just what I was thinking. On the crutches it could say

**Given by the
Agnes McWilliams Aluminum
Crutches Fund."**

"How do we put that on the crutches?" asked Agnes.

"We can get a name tape and stick it on. My dad had one made for his fishing pole. It cost a quarter," said Kevin.

The children ran back to the store, bought the crutches, and went to get the name tape made.

Suddenly Ruth stopped. "We have no quarter," she said. "We spent all the money on the crutches."

"Follow me," said Jack. In less than two minutes they were in front of the store where Lucky was fishing through the grating again.

"Any luck?" asked Jack.

"No," said Lucky. "I got the quarter, okay. But I dropped my Scout knife down there, and I can't get it up."

"Too bad," said Jack. "We made twenty-four dollars and fifty cents. We've bought the crutches already."

Lucky could hardly believe it. Twenty-four dollars and fifty cents! But there were the crutches right before her eyes.

"We need a quarter," Jack said, "for a name tape. We're giving the crutches to the hospital."

"You can't have the quarter," Lucky said. She had lost her knife trying to get the quarter, and she wasn't going to give it up.

"Okay, then," said Jack. "Ruth won't pull up your knife with her magnet."

"Get the knife first," Lucky said. "Then I'll give you the quarter."

Ruth got the magnet and string out of her pocket. She pulled the knife through the grating.

"Thanks," Lucky said. "My luck is sure with me."

The children raced off to the store and made the name tape. The tape said,

The Agnes McWilliams
Alumum Crutches Fund.

Kevin left out the *in* in *aluminum*. But the people at the hospital were very glad to get the crutches.

It had been a lucky day—even for Lucky.

Ruth Adams

Fidelia

PART ONE

The New Violin

Almost everyone in Fidelia's family played an instrument. Her papa played the trumpet with a band. The band played at dances and the annual Mexican-American picnic. Fidelia was proud of her father and his trumpet.

Fidelia's brother and sister played in the school orchestra. Her brother, Alberto, played the trombone, and her sister, Carmela, played the clarinet. The orchestra played for P.T.A. meetings, and once a year the best players were picked to be in the All City Orchestra. Fidelia didn't play anything.

"You will have to wait," said Papa. "I don't have the money to get another instrument right now."

"Your arms aren't long enough to play a trombone," said Alberto.

"You need all your front teeth to play the clarinet," said Carmela.

Fidelia didn't want to play the trombone or the clarinet. She wanted to play the violin.

One morning Fidelia stopped by the music room while the orchestra was practicing. Up and down went Miss Toomey's baton. Fidelia listened to the sounds of the violins. She closed her eyes so she could hear the music better. She started to move closer until she heard a loud crash. She opened her eyes to find that she had knocked over a big drum. Everyone stopped playing and looked at Fidelia.

"What have we here?" asked Miss Toomey.

"That's our sister, Fidelia," said Carmela. "She wants to play in the orchestra."

"Fidelia, come here," said Miss Toomey. "What instrument do you want to play?"

"The violin," whispered Fidelia.

"You're a bit young to play the violin," said Miss Toomey. "But, we need someone to play the tambourine for the song we are practicing. Would you like to try?"

"Yes, thank you," said Fidelia.

The tambourine didn't have the same beautiful sound as the violin. Still, Fidelia did her best. She listened to the beat of the music. She watched Miss Toomey's baton. She learned to start on the downbeat, and she learned how to tell when to stop. But she wished that she could play a violin.

One morning Miss Toomey said, "Boys and girls, Mrs. Reed is coming next week to pick the best players for the All City Orchestra."

Everyone began to talk at once. Miss Toomey called for order.

The orchestra began to practice the song. Fidelia shook her tambourine with a heavy heart. What could she play for Mrs. Reed? If only she had a violin. Then Fidelia had an idea.

On her way home from school, she stopped at a candy store and asked the woman there for a small box. She found one with a lid that was just right.

Down the street, a new building was going up. Fidelia saw a pile of wood and found a board that looked about right. "Please, may I have this board?" she asked one of the workers.

"Take the whole pile if you want it," said the man.

"No, thank you," said Fidelia. "I just want one."

Back home, Fidelia took the box and the board into the garage. She found a hammer and a can filled with nails and tried to nail the lid to the sides of the box. But the nails slid through the board and stuck out. They did not touch the sides of the box at all.

Just then Alberto came into the garage. "What are you doing?" he asked.

"I'm making something," she said. She quickly hid the box and board behind her back.

Alberto looked over Fidelia's shoulder and said, "You need some braces."

He took the hammer and nailed three pieces of wood to the ends of the lid and the middle of the box. Then he nailed the board onto the box. Fidelia watched.

"What's next?" Alberto asked.

"Strings," said Fidelia. "What can I use for strings and pegs?"

"Well, rubber bands for the strings, I think," said Alberto. "But I don't know what to do about pegs. I guess we'll just have to use nails."

"Carmela has a collection of rubber bands," said Fidelia. "I'll go ask her for some."

Fidelia got four rubber bands from Carmela. Alberto nailed four nails at each end of the board on the box to hold them.

Fidelia plucked the rubber bands. "It sounds awful!" she cried.

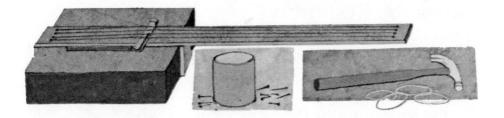

Carmela came into the garage. "If you are trying to make a violin, you need a bridge for the strings to go over. I'll be right back," she said.

Carmela returned with a clothespin. She slid it under the rubber bands. "Now see if you can play a tune," she told Fidelia.

Fidelia placed the violin under her chin and plucked it with the fingers of her right hand. With the fingers of her left hand, she pushed down on the rubber bands.

As Alberto and Carmela left the garage, Fidelia thanked them for helping her. Then she began to practice playing her violin. By dinner time the ends of her fingers hurt. But she knew exactly how to make the sounds she wanted.

PART TWO

A Beginning

The day came for Mrs. Reed to pick the players for the All City Orchestra. Fidelia put her violin into a bag and went to school.

As Fidelia opened the door to the music room, Carmela whispered, "Hurry up! We are going to start practicing the songs. Mrs. Reed is already here."

Fidelia put her bag in the corner and got the tambourine. She watched Miss Toomey's baton carefully. Fidelia played her very best.

Miss Toomey said, "Next, we will play a quiet song."

That was what Fidelia had been waiting for. Quietly she took her violin out of the bag. When she heard the violins, she began to play.

Suddenly Fidelia saw that everyone else had stopped playing. They were all looking at her. She felt hot all over.

"Fidelia, come up here," said Miss Toomey. "What is this?"

"It's a violin that Alberto and Carmela helped me make," Fidelia answered.

Mrs. Reed held out her hand. "Was this your own idea?" she asked Fidelia.

"Yes," answered Fidelia.

"It was a good idea," said Mrs. Reed, "but I'm afraid you cannot play a tune on this violin."

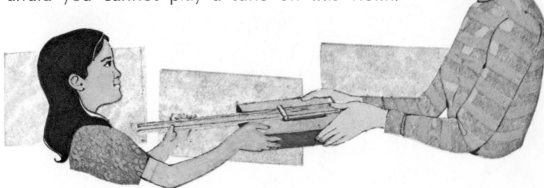

"Oh, but I can play a tune," cried Fidelia. "I've been practicing. I'll show you."

Fidelia plucked away at the rubber bands. When she finished playing, Mrs. Reed asked, "How did you know where to place your fingers on the strings?"

"I watched the others," said Fidelia.

"Would you like to play a real violin?" Mrs. Reed asked.

"Oh, yes! But I am too little," said Fidelia.

Mrs. Reed went out of the room and came back with the smallest violin case any of the children had ever seen. As she opened the case she said, "This is a quarter-size violin, boys and girls. Let's see how it fits Fidelia."

It fit Fidelia exactly right.

"Fidelia," said Mrs. Reed, "the boy who used this violin needs a larger size, so I am going to leave it here for you to use. Miss Toomey will start you in the beginning string class. I will come back in a few weeks to see how you are doing."

Fidelia put the little violin under her chin. She set the bow on the strings. "I'm ready, Miss Toomey," she said.

"Beginning string class meets after lunch, Fidelia. You'll have to wait," said Miss Toomey.

Alberto played his trombone and Carmela played her clarinet in the All City Orchestra, but Fidelia didn't mind. She had a violin exactly her size, and she was in the beginning string class.

Everyone has to start somewhere.

WORD PICTURES

The way you use words depends on what you are trying to do. Below are two ways to tell about a sunrise. Which one might be heard on the radio in the morning? Which one was written by the poet Emily Dickinson?

The sun rose at 6:15 A.M.

I'll tell you how the sun rose
A ribbon at a time.

Which of these sentences paint word pictures? Which ones tell facts?

Mama was angry.
There was fire in Mama's eyes.

Agnes had the fastest crutches in the West.
Agnes moved fast on her crutches.

Mitzi Tanaka

SEIGO'S SPECIAL NAME

Gail and Seigo aren't just sister and brother. They are best friends. They talk and laugh with each other. They plan surprises for their friends. They help each other when they can.

One day Seigo came home from school with a mad face. Gail listened as Seigo told her why. "People think that my name is funny. They can't say it right. It makes me wish that Mother and Dad hadn't given me a Japanese name."

Gail said, "You were given a special name. It's Great-Grandfather's name. I wonder what we can do so people will say it right?"

They thought and thought for a long time. Then Gail's eyes grew bright. "I have an idea!" she said. As she told Seigo, he became more and more excited. There was a smile on his face.

The next day Gail and Seigo got up early. They went to their father's room. Seigo asked him to paint some things for them. Gail told Dad what to paint.

Then they got ready for school and ate their breakfast. Gail and Seigo ran to school. They smiled because they had a plan. Once at school they went to different rooms. Seigo said he would tell Gail all that happened.

Before class, Seigo talked to his teacher. He said he had something to show and tell the class. She said that there would be time before lunch. Seigo waited and when the time came, he went to the front of the room. With him he carried a large flat package.

"Today I have something to show you. It will tell you a lot about me. It is here in this package. Can anyone guess what it is?"

"Is it a kite?" asked one child.

"No," said Seigo. "Guess again."

"Is it a picture?" asked another child.

"Yes," said Seigo. "But can you guess what it is a picture of?" No one could guess. So Seigo untied the package.

There was the beautiful picture which Gail and his father had done. It was a picture of a ship.

"A long, long time ago," Seigo began, "my great-grandfather came to America from Japan. He came on a ship like this one. My great-grandmother came later. They left Japan to start a new life in the United States. Together they made a good living on their farm. We are Japanese-Americans. My family is special.

"My great-grandfather could do many things other than farm. He told stories and painted pictures, too. My great-grandmother wrote songs and music. My grandmother can cook anything from spaghetti to chocolate cake. She lives with us."

Seigo went on with his story.

"My mother is in records. She picks out and buys the records for stores in town. My Dad is an art director at the museum. I asked him to do this picture."

"You must be very proud," said one of the girls.

"On the back of the picture are the letters of my name in Japanese. They are the same as the ones in my great-grandfather's name. Our lives as Japanese-Americans began when my great-grandfather came here. I'm proud to have his name."

And Seigo said his name loud and clear, "Say-Go."

Other children in the class said things about their families.

Joan said, "My mother says that I'm Irish and German."

Collin said, "My grandfather came from Cuba."

Susan said, "I'm Jewish-American."

Lara said, "I don't know what I am."

"Lara, you might ask your mother or father what you are," the teacher said. "Then, if you wish, you can tell *us* what you are. Seigo is Japanese-American. Seigo, I learned something about you and your name today. Thank you."

It was time for lunch. Seigo walked out of the classroom with a smile. People were saying his name right.

He saw Gail eating lunch with a friend. Seigo went over. He said, "It worked. Now people are saying my name right. I'll tell you more later."

Before he ran off to join his friends, he said to himself, "Thank you, Great-Grandfather. I like my name a lot."

My Name

I wrote my name on the sidewalk
But the rain washed it away.

I wrote my name on my hand
But the soap washed it away.

I wrote my name on the birthday card
I gave to Mother today

And there it will stay
For mother never throws
                    ANYTHING

of mine away!

— Lee Bennett Hopkins

The Talking Leaves

Bernice Kohn

A long time ago, when the United States was young, there lived a Cherokee boy named Sequoyah. He was not as tall as his friends, and he was lame. Yet this small lame boy grew up to be the greatest Cherokee of them all. For it was Sequoyah who solved the mystery of the talking leaves.

PART ONE

The Mystery

Sequoyah was born about 1773. No one knows for sure just which year it was. In those days the Indians did not have a written language.

Sequoyah's mother was the daughter of a great Cherokee chief. His father was an Englishman named Nathaniel Gist. Nathaniel left the Cherokees soon after Sequoyah was born. He had to go back to his own people. But Sequoyah and his mother stayed with the tribe. That was the custom.

When he was a boy, Sequoyah became very sick and almost died. He got well. But after his sickness, one leg was weak and shorter than the other. Sequoyah hunted less. He began to make use of his strong hands.

Sequoyah started to paint animals and carve them in wood. Soon he could carve the masks that the men in his tribe wore. Later he learned to make strong iron pots for his mother.

By the time Sequoyah was a young man, he was able to make beautiful necklaces and rings. When he married, he built a house and a spinning wheel for his young wife.

Sequoyah and his wife had five children. First four sons were born, and then a daughter. The little girl was named Ah-yoka.

As a young man, Sequoyah traveled a great deal. He met many people. Sequoyah was interested in the language that the White people spoke. But he was even more interested in their reading and writing.

The White people used paper on which to write. Sequoyah thought that paper looked like large white leaves. The "leaves" were covered with many black marks. Sequoyah watched the people as they looked at their "leaves." To Sequoyah it seemed as though the little marks written on the paper were *talking* to the people.

Sequoyah never forgot the mystery of the talking leaves. He made up his mind that if leaves could talk, then he would make them talk for the Cherokee people.

Sequoyah tried to make a picture for every word he could think of. He made the signs on pieces of bark. He made picture signs for horses and colts and pots and every other thing he knew. In a very short time, he had so many signs no one could remember them all. Even Sequoyah was getting mixed up. There had to be a better way.

Sequoyah thought and thought, and then one day the idea came. Of course! All words are made up of sounds. He didn't need a sign for every word but only one for every sound. By putting the sounds together, he could make any word.

Sequoyah set to work right away to find out how many sounds there were in the Cherokee language. He said each sound out loud. His friends began to look at him strangely.

Then Sequoyah found a book written in English. Maybe from it he could learn the magic of the talking leaves. He would write some of the letters on pieces of bark. A few of them looked better upside down or on their sides, so he made them that way.

Sequoyah worked night and day. The pile of bark grew higher and higher. But Sequoyah didn't care about anything else.

Some of the Cherokees could not understand what Sequoyah was doing. They began to talk against him. One said that Sequoyah was making bad magic for the tribe. Sequoyah's wife became angry at Sequoyah. She picked up all the bark and threw it in the fire.

At first Sequoyah was very upset, but he started to work all over again. At last Sequoyah was finished. He had made a sign for each of the syllables in the Cherokee language. Sequoyah had made a syllabary.

A syllabary has a sign for every syllable. There were eighty-six signs in Sequoyah's syllabary.

But now what? Could other Cherokees learn to use the syllabary? His little daughter could already read it and write it. But what about the others? Would they care? Would they *want* to learn?

Sequoyah thought the time had come to find out if all the years of hard work had been worth it. It was 1821, and it was time to make a test.

The Test

Sequoyah went to the head of the Cherokee tribe, and a meeting was called. Word of Sequoyah's talking leaves went through the tribe. The meeting room was soon filled with excited people.

Sequoyah was sent out of the room with two guards. They made sure that Sequoyah could not hear what was happening in the room.

Inside, the chiefs gave messages to Sequoyah's daughter, Ah-yoka. Nothing could be heard in the room but Ah-yoka's quill pen as she quickly began writing the messages.

At last Sequoyah was called back into the room. He took the paper from his daughter's hand and read the messages in a clear, loud voice. It worked! The Cherokee people had a written language!

Now everyone wanted to learn the new syllabary at once. Little children and wise old people worked together to learn it.

During the next year Sequoyah helped show many Cherokees how to teach the syllabary. By 1828 the Cherokee people had their own newspaper and books and schools. Cherokee children could learn to read and write.

Of course, everyone was very proud of Sequoyah. Not only the Cherokees but the whole country was proud of him. Never before had just one person made up a written language. Even the President of the United States heard of what Sequoyah had done. To show how proud he was of Sequoyah, the President gave him a gift of $500.00 a year for the rest of his life.

But what pleased Sequoyah most was a beautiful silver medal with his picture on it. It was given to him by his own people. He wore the medal around his neck for the rest of his life.

When Sequoyah heard about some Cherokees in Mexico, he wondered if they could use the syllabary, too. He made up his mind to go and look for them.

Sequoyah set out for Mexico in 1842. It was a long and hard trip on foot and on horseback. The trip was much too hard for an old man. Shortly after he got to Mexico, Sequoyah became very sick and died.

The Cherokee people and the whole country were sad. Everyone knew they had lost a great and wise man.

Today the tallest trees in the world, the giant redwoods, are called sequoias. They are named for the small lame boy who became the greatest Cherokee of them all—the man who brought a great gift to his people—the written word.

4 OTHER PLACES

Five Hundred Thousand Miles

Five hundred thousand miles away
Someone is doing something today,
And I wonder what he is doing today
Five hundred thousand miles away.

Five hundred thousand miles away
Maybe he's laughing and singing today,
Or maybe he's sad and lonely today.
Five hundred thousand miles away.

Five hundred thousand miles away
I wonder if someone like me today
Is wond'ring what I am doing today
Five hundred thousand miles away.

—*Marci Ridlon*

Tikki Tikki Tembo

Arlene Mosel

Once upon a time, a long, long time ago,
all the fathers and mothers in China
used to give their first and honored sons
great long names. But second sons were
given hardly any name at all.

In a small mountain village there lived a
mother who had two little sons. Her
second son she called Chang, which means
"little or nothing." But her first and
honored son, she called **Tikki tikki tembo-
no sa rembo-chari bari ruchi-pip peri
pembo.** It means "the most wonderful
thing in the whole wide world!"

Every morning the mother went to wash
in a little stream near her home. The two
boys always went along with her. On the
bank was an old well.

"Don't go near the well," the mother told them, "or you will surely fall in."

The boys did not always mind their mother. One day they were playing beside the well and on the well when Chang fell in!

Tikki tikki tembo-no sa rembo-chari bari ruchi-pip peri pembo ran to his mother as fast as his little legs could carry him.

"Most Honorable Mother," he gasped, "Chang has fallen into the well!"

"The water roars, Priceless Jewel. I cannot hear you," said the mother.

Then Tikki tikki tembo-no sa rembo-chari bari ruchi-pip peri pembo raised his voice.

"Oh, Most Honorable One," he cried, **"Chang has fallen into the well!"**

"That troublesome boy," answered the mother. "Run and get the Old Man With The Ladder to fish him out."

Then Tikki tikki tembo-no sa rembo-chari bari ruchi-pip peri pembo ran as fast as his little legs could carry him to the Old Man With The Ladder.

"Old Man With The Ladder," he gasped, "Chang has fallen into the well. Will you come and fish him out?"

"So," said the Old Man With The Ladder, "Chang has fallen into the well."

And he ran as fast as his old legs could carry him. Step over step, step over step, he went into the well and picked up little Chang. And step over step, step over step, he brought him out of the well.

He pumped the water out of him and pushed the air into him, and pumped the water out of him and pushed the air into him. And soon Chang was just as good as ever!

Now for the next few months the boys went with their mother to wash, but they did not go near the well. One day, however, they ran to the well to eat their rice cakes.

They ate near the well. They played around the well. They walked on the well. And Tikki tikki tembo-no sa rembo-chari bari ruchi-pip peri pembo fell into the well!

Chang ran as fast as his little legs could carry him to the stream where his mother had gone to wash.

"Oh, Most Honorable Mother," he gasped, "Tikki tikki tembo-no sa rembo-chari bari ruchi-pip peri pembo has fallen into the well!"

"The water roars, Little One. Speak up. I cannot hear you," said the mother.

So little Chang took a deep breath and raised his voice.

"Oh, Mother, Most Honorable," he shouted, **"Tikki tikki tembo-no sa rembo-chari bari ruchi-pip peri pembo has fallen into the well!"**

"Troublesome Child, didn't you hear me tell you to speak up? The water roars. What are you trying to say?" said his mother.

**"Honorable Mother!
Chari bari
rembo
tikki tikki,"**
he gasped,
"pip pip has fallen into the well!"

"My Poor Son, honor your brother. Speak his name carefully," said the mother.

Poor little Chang was all out of breath from saying that great long name, and he didn't think he could say it one more time. But then he thought of his brother in the old well.

Chang bowed his little head clear to the sand and took a deep breath.

Slowly, very slowly, in a raised voice he said, **"Most Honorable Mother, Tikki tikki tembo-no sa rembo-chari bari ruchi-pip peri pembo is at the bottom of the well."**

"Oh, not my first and honored son, my Priceless Jewel! Run quickly and tell the Old Man With The Ladder that your brother has fallen into the well," said the mother.

So Chang ran as fast as his little legs
would carry him to the Old Man With
The Ladder. Under a tree the Old Man
With The Ladder sat bowed and silent.

"**Old Man, Old Man,**" shouted Chang,
"**come right away! Tikki tikki tembo-no sa
rembo-chari bari ruchi-pip peri pembo
has fallen into the stone well!**"

But there was no answer. For a second
Chang waited. Then with his very last
bit of breath he shouted, "**Old Man
With The Ladder, Tikki tikki tembo-no
sa rembo-chari bari ruchi-pip peri pembo
is at the bottom of the well.**"

"Troublesome child, you wake me from
a wonderful dream. I had floated into a
deep blue mist and found myself young
again. There were beautiful flowers
and jewels. If I close my eyes, the dream
may again return."

Poor little Chang was frightened. How could he say that long name again? He bowed clear to the ground.

"Please, Old Man With The Ladder," he cried, "please help my brother out of the cold well."

"So," said the Old Man With The Ladder, "your mother's Priceless Jewel has fallen into the well!"

The Old Man With The Ladder hurried as fast as his old legs could carry him. Step over step, step over step, he went into the well. And step over step, step over step, he came out of the well with the little boy in his arms. Then he pumped the water out of him and pushed the air into him, and pumped the water out of him and pushed the air into him.

But little Tikki tikki tembo-no sa
rembo-chari bari ruchi-pip peri pembo had
been in the water so long, all because of
his great long name, that it was many
weeks before he was quite the same again.

And from that day to this the fathers
and mothers of China have always thought
it wise to give all their children little
short names rather than great long names.

The Optimist

The optimist fell ten stories,
And at each window bar
He shouted to the folks inside:
"Doing all right so far!"

—Anonymous

Gumdrop on the Move

Val Biro

PART ONE

Mr. Oldcastle Finds Gumdrop

Mr. Oldcastle liked old cars. He had a small brown car, a 1934 Austin. He kept it in a garage with a green door. There was another little garage with a red door. But it had no car in it.

"In there," he said to his grandson Robert, "I had another car once. It was blue with a black top and a shiny horn."

Then he said, "That was a real vintage Austin — a 1926. I had to sell it years ago."

Just then the mail came. There, with all the letters, was a notice about "The Auction of Vintage Cars." And on the first page was a picture.

Mr. Oldcastle became very excited. *"Look!"* he said. *"Here it is! This is the very car that I had all those years ago. It must be Gumdrop!"*

And it was. When Mr. Oldcastle went to the auction the next day, there, sure enough, was Gumdrop. Many people wanted to buy it.

Mr. Carstairs wanted Gumdrop because he had a collection of vintage cars. Mr. Banger wanted Gumdrop because he sold cars. And Mr. Oldcastle wanted Gumdrop because he once owned it himself.

The auction began. One after another people bid. The one who bid the most got the car.

Many cars were sold this way until it was Gumdrop's turn. "What am I bid for this wonderful car?" shouted the man in charge of the auction.

People bid quickly for Gumdrop, and the price got higher and higher. At last the man cried, "Going, going, gone! Sold to Mr. Banger!"

Mr. Carstairs did not buy it after all because Gumdrop wasn't rare enough for him. "And I couldn't buy it," said Mr. Oldcastle sadly to Robert, "because Gumdrop wasn't cheap enough for me."

Mr. Banger cleaned Gumdrop until it shone. Then he put it with all the new cars in the window of his showroom. "This old car should help to sell my new cars," he said.

Many people stopped to look at Gumdrop, but only a few of them bought new cars. Mr. Banger was disappointed.

Arthur Carson came into the shop one day. "Will you sell me that blue vintage Austin there? I want to race it at Silverstone," he said.

"I might as well," said Mr. Banger, "because after all the car isn't new enough for me."

So Arthur took Gumdrop to his garage. There he removed the top so that Gumdrop could go faster. He took off the shiny horn and put it into the toolbox. Next day he raced Gumdrop at Silverstone.

The vintage cars were tearing around the course. Gumdrop went faster and faster, but the other cars went faster and faster still. Suddenly there was a noise in the engine. Gumdrop stopped.

"That's the front end!" cried Arthur. "I'm out of the race!" He was very disappointed.

Rocky Crasher came to help push Gumdrop off the course. "I'll buy this car from you," he said. "I want to race it at Brightstar."

"You can have it," said Arthur, "because after all the car isn't fast enough for me."

Rocky took Gumdrop to his garage so he could fix the front end. Then he removed the fenders and lamps to make Gumdrop light. And he painted the car yellow with green stripes.

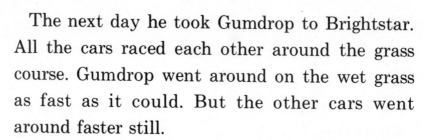

The next day he took Gumdrop to Brightstar.
All the cars raced each other around the grass
course. Gumdrop went around on the wet grass
as fast as it could. But the other cars went
around faster still.

Suddenly Gumdrop spun around and stopped.
"My wheel has come off!" cried Rocky. "I'm out
of the race!" He was very disappointed.

Sandy Boardman came to help with the wheel.
"Will you sell me your car?" he asked. "I want
to race it at the Bridgetown-hill-climb."

"I will," said Rocky Crasher, "because after
all the car isn't light enough for me."

So Sandy Boardman took Gumdrop to his
garage. There he removed the running boards
and the extra wheel. He then oiled Gumdrop for
the big hill-climb.

The next day Sandy and Gumdrop were at
Bridgetown. The other cars raced up the hill
with roaring engines. Gumdrop went as fast as
it could, but the hill was too much for it.
Gumdrop's engine was roaring, too, until there
was steam coming out of the front end, and
Gumdrop had to stop.

"We're out of the race!" cried Sandy. He was very disappointed.

Farmer Small came to help with a can of water. "That's a handy car you've got there," he said. "It would help me on the farm."

"You can have it," said Sandy Boardman, "because after all the car isn't strong enough for me."

So Mr. Small took Gumdrop to his farm. There he removed the number plates. Then he took out the back seat to make room for the corn and the straw that he wanted Gumdrop to carry. Even so, there wasn't enough room. Mr. Small was very disappointed.

"I'll just have to leave it in the yard," he said, "because after all the car isn't big enough for me."

Gumdrop stayed at the farm. Without a top, horn, lamps, fenders, running boards, extra wheel, number plates, back seat, or doors, Gumdrop was a strange and sorry sight.

PART TWO

Gumdrop Finds a Home

One day Mike Manson saw Gumdrop. When Mr. Small came by, Mike asked him about the car. "You can have this old car. I have no use for it," said Mr. Small.

"Thanks," Mike said, jumping into Gumdrop.

Mike Manson drove badly and too fast. He bumped into a small brown car that was standing by the roadside. It was Mr. Oldcastle's baby Austin of 1934. Mr. Oldcastle was there himself.

"Look where you're going," he shouted. "You've put a dent in my car, and you nearly got me!"

Mike was scared. "I'm sorry," he said. "I can't pay for what I've done to your car. Tell you what. You can have this old car!" Without waiting for an answer, he jumped over the fence and ran away. After all, Gumdrop wasn't worth enough for Mike.

Mr. Oldcastle looked at Gumdrop. "Strange-looking car," he said, "though it is a vintage Austin. And I could restore it. It would be wonderful to have a vintage Austin again." So he tied Gumdrop to his car and drove home.

The next day Mr. Oldcastle and Robert drove to the junkyard to look for the missing parts for Gumdrop. Old cars were piled up everywhere.

"Funny you should ask me," said Alexander Horn, the junkman. "Quite a lot of vintage Austin parts have come in lately. You can have the lot."

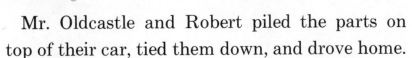

Mr. Oldcastle and Robert piled the parts on top of their car, tied them down, and drove home.

Then they began to restore the car. They put back the fenders, the running boards, the lamps, and the doors. They put on the top and put in the back seat. They put the extra wheel in place. Then they painted the body blue and the fenders black. After a week of hard work, the car looked as good as new.

"It looks exactly like my old car now," said Mr. Oldcastle. "I wish this car were really Gumdrop."

Just then Robert was looking in the toolbox while Mr. Oldcastle cleaned the engine. "I wonder," he thought, "if after all..." He looked at the engine number. C4478. *"The same!"* he shouted. *"The same number! This must really be..."*

"It is! It is!" shouted Robert in turn, as he pulled out the shiny horn. *"This is our own Gumdrop after all!"*

So Mr. Oldcastle got Gumdrop back again. He drove proudly to the town the next week to take part in the Vintage Car Show. Farmer Small was there, and he gave Mr. Oldcastle Gumdrop's number plates which he had taken off. The Mayor was there, and he gave Mr. Oldcastle a silver cup for "The Best Restored Vintage Car."

And there, too, were all the people who had owned Gumdrop since the Vintage Auction. They came up to shake hands with Mr. Oldcastle.

There was Mr. Carstairs, for whom Gumdrop wasn't rare enough. There was Mr. Banger, for whom Gumdrop wasn't new enough.

There was Arthur Carson, for whom Gumdrop wasn't fast enough. There was Rocky Crasher, for whom Gumdrop wasn't light enough.

There was Sandy Boardman, for whom Gumdrop wasn't strong enough. There was Farmer Small, for whom Gumdrop wasn't big enough. There was Mike Manson, for whom Gumdrop wasn't worth enough.

And there was Mr. Oldcastle, who got his old car back. For him Gumdrop was worth more than enough.

The Golden Treasure

Maryke Reesink

Long ago, there was a seaport called Stavoren. From this seaport ships sailed all over the world, bringing back many treasures.

There was one family in the town that had great wealth. They had only one child, a little girl. She had dolls and toys of all kinds to play with and pretty clothes to wear. Still, she was never happy and always wanted more.

When she grew up, she owned more ships than anyone else. She lived in the biggest house in Stavoren. Still, she was not happy. She wasn't very kind, and people called her "Proud Lady."

One night a wild storm blew up, bringing ships at sea into the port of Stavoren.

Alone in her big house, with the wind tearing at the windows and the door, sat the Proud Lady. Suddenly, someone knocked loud and long at the door. In came a sea captain.

"Why have you come here on such a night?" asked the lady.

"For years I have sailed the high seas," he answered. "Always I have heard that your ships are the biggest and the best. This storm blew my ship into your port. Now that I am here I would like to sail one of your ships wherever you wish."

Because the lady always sent her ships on long hard trips, most men did not like to work for her. She liked the looks of this sea captain, so she said, "My new ship, *The Golden Treasure,* needs a skipper. He must be a man who will sail the seas, to places where no ship has gone before. And he must bring back to me whatever is most precious in the whole world."

The skipper was silent for a long time. Then he said slowly, "If you will give me *The Golden Treasure,* I will sail her over the seas and the oceans until I have found what is most precious on earth. Then I will bring it back to you."

"Then sail tomorrow!" said the lady.

T he next day *The Golden Treasure* set sail.

After many weeks it reached a place known for its beautiful glass. The people in this town made great balls of glass so light they seemed to float in the air like balloons.

The skipper thought how beautiful these glass balls would be in the lady's house. Still, something even more precious might be found, so he set sail again to keep looking.

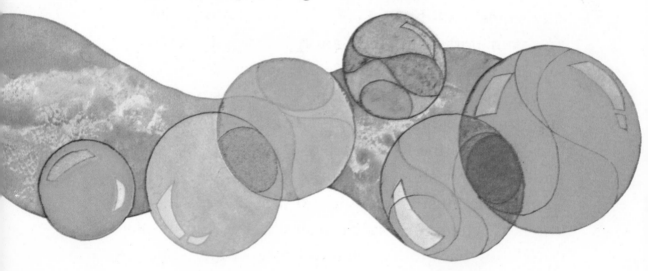

Months and months went by, and at last *The Golden Treasure* came to a country where all the people wore silk clothes. Beautiful silks filled the shops. For children, there were dolls so lifelike they seemed almost like children themselves.

The captain and his crew couldn't believe their eyes. Then the captain remembered that the lady had a beautiful silk dress. And since she had no children to love the dolls, he did not buy anything. *The Golden Treasure* set sail again.

The weather got hotter and hotter. At last, there was no more water on board for the crew, so *The Golden Treasure* sailed into a quiet lagoon. A stream of clear water ran into the lagoon, and coconuts and fruits of all kinds grew on trees near the shore. These would be treasures to fill the lady's silver dishes. But there might be something even more precious in another place. So *The Golden Treasure* sailed out of the lagoon.

For weeks and weeks the captain and his crew sailed without seeing land. They began to run out of food, and the men were hungry and sick.

At last the lookout called, "Land!" And the next day *The Golden Treasure* sailed up a wide river. On either side lay fields of golden wheat. Where there is wheat, there is bread. The hungry men could eat again!

The skipper let the golden grain run through his fingers. This was the most precious thing in the whole world, for it would give food to hungry people everywhere.

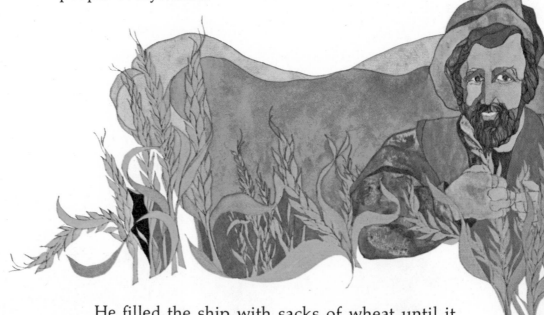

He filled the ship with sacks of wheat until it could hold no more. Then he sailed for Stavoren.

Every day for three years, the lady had gone to the shore to look for *The Golden Treasure*. She dreamed of the great wealth it would bring her and never noticed there were poor and hungry people in the town. At last one morning, *The Golden Treasure* sailed into port.

"What have you brought me?" the lady called to the captain.

"Gold!" he answered. "Golden wheat—the most precious thing in the world!"

When the lady saw that there were no furs, no silk or gold or silver, only ugly sacks of grain, she was very angry. She turned to the captain and said, "You call this precious! Throw it overboard—all of it!"

"It is wheat—bread for the hungry," said the captain to the proud lady.

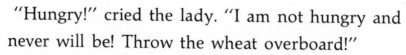

"Hungry!" cried the lady. "I am not hungry and never will be! Throw the wheat overboard!"

Though the townspeople asked her to stop it, one by one the sacks of wheat were thrown overboard and sank to the bottom of the sea. Then the lady turned to the skipper, but he had disappeared.

As time went by, the wheat began to grow. It grew until it reached above the water, but no grain ever grew on the plants.

The growing wheat held sand and mud in place so that the port of Stavoren filled up with it. Ships could no longer sail in.

Most of the townspeople moved to other places. The people who stayed became very poor.

At last, even the Proud Lady had to leave. Many of her ships had been lost at sea. She had sold all her treasures for food. Nothing was left of her great wealth. As poor and hungry as anyone else, she went from village to village looking for bread and a place to sleep.

She thought many times of the sacks of wheat that had been thrown into the sea. Then she had had bread and was not hungry.

ne night, she came to a small town. Seeing a man at a door, she started toward him. As she got closer to him, she thought he was someone she had known before. All at once she was sure. It was the captain.

The lady bowed her head and said, "I should have given the wheat to the people who were hungry."

"You know now that there is nothing more precious in all the world," said the captain. Then he took her into his house and gave her a chair by the fire.

But to this day the seaport of Stavoren is filled with mud and sand, and no proud ships sail in or out.

Same Sound - Different Words

Some words sound just the same but are spelled differently and have different meanings. Look at the underlined words in each pair of sentences. Match the sentences with the pictures.

You are pretty, dear.
You are pretty, deer.

Did you see that sail?
Did you see that sale?

Use these words in sentences.

piece	hole	meat
peace	whole	meet

Barbara K. Walker

The Round Sultan and the Straight Answer

PART ONE

The Sultan Who Loved to Eat

Once there was a sultan who loved to eat. Three or four times a day he ate. One after another, he ate

yogurt soup
and rice with yogurt
and meats with yogurt
and fruits with yogurt.

Great heaps of dark brown bread just melted away.

Mealtimes were wonderful. Music was played. Birds sang in their cages.

Each day, the sultan looked in the mirror. He smiled to see that he was growing at last to be a fine big sultan. He must surely be the fattest, roundest sultan in all the world, he thought.

One day the sultan found that he was too fat to walk a step. His feet hurt if he stood up, even for a minute. His royal throne got a crack, and a new one had to be made.

One by one, the sultan's royal shirts and royal pants tore. He had to have all new clothes, much larger than his old ones.

The sultan could no longer fit into the royal bathtub. A new one was made, large enough to hold two elephants. Ten men helped the sultan into the bathtub. Ten men helped the sultan out again.

Clearly, the sultan had become too fat.
Something had to be done.

A crier went out all over the
kingdom.

HEAR YE!   HEAR YE!
*The sultan has become too fat. He must
have a doctor to help him become thin
again. Who can help the sultan? Your
prize will be great.*

Doctors hurried to the castle from all
parts of the kingdom. Each one was sure
he could help the sultan.

The first doctor looked at the sultan.
Then he said, "My Sultan, you must
eat nothing but fruit."

The sultan tried for a week to eat
nothing but fruit. He had fruit for
breakfast, lunch, afternoon tea, and
dinner. He tried to eat nothing but fruit.
Oh, he ate between meals now and
then. A pile of rice with meat made a
fine snack. And nothing was better
than a few plates of honey cakes.

At the end of a week, the first doctor came to see the sultan. The sultan was fatter than ever.

"To the dungeon with him!" shouted the sultan. **"Give him nothing but fruit. As for me, fruit just won't do."**

A second doctor looked at the sultan. Then he said, "My Sultan, you must take nothing but hot tea."

The sultan tried for a week to take nothing but hot tea. He had hot tea for breakfast, hot tea for lunch, hot tea for afternoon tea, and then hot tea for dinner. Oh, he ate between meals now and then, because he was so hungry. A pile of rice with meat made a fine snack. And he did love honey cakes.

At the end of the week, the second doctor came to see the sultan. The sultan was fatter than ever.

"To the dungeon with him!" shouted the sultan. **"Give him nothing but hot tea. As for me, hot tea just won't do."**

More doctors came. "Give the sultan steam baths every day," said one.

The sultan had one steam bath after another for a week. Between baths he ate and ate. Off to the dungeon went another doctor.

"Nothing but meat!" said one doctor. "Smaller helpings!" said the next doctor. "No music at meals!" said another. "Less sleep!" "Nothing but yogurt!" "Give him these special pills!"

One after another, forty doctors tried to help the sultan. One after another, forty doctors went off to the dungeon.

As for the sultan, he grew even fatter.

The Forty Days

One day a wise hamal passed the castle. On his back he carried the furniture of a whole house.

"Hamal!" called the sultan's page. "You are needed in the castle."

The hamal set down the furniture. He hurried after the page until he came before the sultan.

"You can carry the furniture from a whole house," said the page. "Lift our sultan into his bed."

For a minute the hamal looked at the sultan. He knew of the sultan's troubles.

"What does it matter if he sits on his throne or gets into his bed? He will be dead in another forty days anyway!" the hamal said.

The sultan gasped. **"How dare you!"** Then in a soft voice he asked,

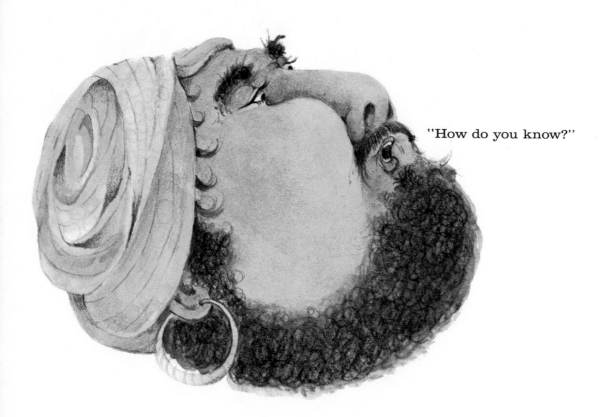

"How do you know?"

"I just **know,**" answered the hamal. "Believe me. You will be dead in forty days."

"He is lying! To the dungeon!" shouted the sultan.

Two men grabbed the hamal and pushed him down the dungeon steps.

As for the sultan, suddenly he was not hungry at all. At breakfast he ate a little brown bread. At lunch he had fruit. At afternoon tea he had a little honey cake. At dinner he ate a small piece of meat. As for eating between meals, somehow food didn't look good to him.

Day after day passed. The sultan sat and worried. At the end of twenty days he got up. His feet felt funny, but he could walk again. He walked the floor hour after hour. Only twenty more days!

His royal shirts and his royal pants began to hang funny. Something strange had happened to them. They were much too big.

At the end of thirty-nine days, the sultan made out his last will. He passed the kingdom on to his younger brother. Who would have thought that the fattest sultan in the world would have ended in such a way?

The last of the forty days came and went. All day the sultan walked the floor. He looked out at the houses below. How sad to leave such a fine kingdom!

The forty-first day came. It was sunny and bright. Birds sang in the trees of the sultan's garden. Suddenly the sultan sat up. This was the forty-first day! He was not dead!

"Send for that hamal!" he cried.

The page hurried down the stone steps to the dungeon. Forty doctors, all of them thin, bowed as he came in.

"This is the forty-first day," said the hamal.

"You are right," said the page. "And the sultan has sent for you."

The hamal followed the page up the steps.

"There you are!" cried the sultan, sitting up in bed. "You said I was to die in forty days. This is the forty-first day. You were lying!"

"That may be," answered the hamal. Then his eyes shone. "But see, My Sultan, **you are thin!**"

For a minute the sultan could not say a word. Then a great smile came over his face. He leaped out of bed. He danced about the room in his royal pajamas. He felt his thin arms, his thin legs, his thin neck. Yes, he was thin.

"Bring me some new scales!" he shouted.

The biggest scales in the kingdom were brought to the sultan. The sultan sat down in the dish at one side of the large scales.

"Now fill up the other dish with gold until the scales are even," ordered the sultan.

The other dish was filled with gold until the great pile was even with the smiling sultan.

"This gold, hamal, is your prize," said the sultan. "Take it, and may your way be open."

The hamal took his treasure with a thankful heart and left the castle.

One by one, the forty doctors climbed the stone steps and went about their work.

As for the sultan, he became no fatter than a sultan should be. And as far as I know, he is a sultan to this day.

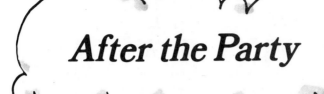

After the Party

Jonathan Blake
Ate too much cake,
He isn't himself today;
He's tucked up in bed
With a feverish head,
And he doesn't much care to play.

I'm sorry to state
That he also ate
Six pickles, a pie, and a pear;
In fact I confess
It's a reasonable guess
He ate practically everything there.

Yes, Jonathan Blake
Ate too much cake,
So he's not at his best today;
But there's no need for sorrow—
If you come back tomorrow,
I'm sure he'll be out to play.

—William Wise

THE ONCE-A-YEAR DAY

Eve Bunting

The short Alaskan summer was almost over.
Annie looked across the dark waters of the bay.
Soon snow would fall and the sea would turn into
ice. Then the village would be closed in from the
outside world once again. Annie touched the
coins in her pocket and counted them. She had
heard on the radio that the big ship was on its
way to the village. Soon the barges would be here.

Suddenly she saw the two barges coming across
the bay. She picked up her pail filled with berries
and began to run. The barges had come! This was
the . . . wonderful, wonderful, wonderful
once-a-year day!

Annie was almost halfway down the hill when
she remembered Emma. Suddenly she was filled
with anger.

"Emma!" she called. "Where are you, Emma?"
That silly Emma! Annie went back up the hill.
"Emma! Emma!"

She saw Emma sitting on the grass. Her pail
held only a few berries.

"Emma!" Annie cried. "Is that all you've got?"

Emma just looked at Annie. She was twelve
years old, one year younger than Annie. But she
was much smaller. Emma was Annie's cousin. She
was now an orphan and had come to live at
Annie's house a few months ago.

Annie started down the hill. "The barges have
come," she said. Emma followed without saying a
word. Many people had already gathered at the
shore. The first barge was almost in.

"It will be fun for you to have a sister," Annie's
mother had said.

It hadn't been fun for Annie. Emma had been no
help at all when they went egging. Annie's father
and her brothers, Daniel and Thomas, had
climbed the steep hills near the village. They had
looked for sea gull eggs. Emma just sat alone.
Even when an angry sea gull flew down suddenly,
Emma had sat quietly.

Emma wasn't any help during the goose hunt either. When two of the geese ran away from the net, Emma didn't even try to stop them. Didn't she know that they needed the geese for food?

"It will be all right," Annie's mother said. "Emma just needs time to get used to living with us." Annie didn't want to think about Emma anymore. This was the once-a-year day.

They were down the hill now. They could hear the motors bringing in the barges.

Annie called to Emma. "This is the once-a-year day when the big ship brings supplies from Seattle. The barges bring the supplies from the ship to us."

Mr. Odark, the storekeeper, had an old truck waiting near the bay. He bought most of the supplies for the village.

Annie's two brothers were pulling on the first barge to get it into the mud. This barge carried big oil drums. This oil was needed to heat the houses and the school. Soon the empty barge moved out.

The second barge was coming in. Would it be on this one? Annie thought. No. This barge carried wooden boxes filled with fishnets, harpoons, and dog harnesses.

When Annie looked again, she saw that the first barge was coming back. This must be it! Her hand closed around the coins in her pocket. She counted them carefully once more.

This time, the first barge was filled with sacks of food. Suddenly Annie saw it—the big wooden box with the one word in black. Annie took a deep breath. It was finally here.

She only had to wait until Mr. Odark got everything he needed up to his store. Soon the barge was empty. The second barge would not come back again. There was nothing else to bring.

Most of the people watched carefully as the barge pulled away from the shore. Everyone was very, very quiet as the barge disappeared from sight. Goodbye, Annie thought. Goodbye barges, goodbye big ship. Don't forget to come back next year.

The truck was filled. Annie looked until she
found the box with the black letters. It wouldn't
be long now.

Annie ran up the hill. She didn't see Emma, and
she was glad. Nobody knew about the thirty cents
she had saved.

Annie went into Mr. Odark's store. Many people
were inside. She saw the wooden box on the
floor. "Will you open this one next?" she asked
Mr. Odark.

"All right, Annie. We'll open it now."

"Can I have the first one?" Annie took the coins
from her pocket.

Mr. Odark held out his big hand and Annie put
the coins into it.

It seemed to Annie that everyone in the room gasped when the wooden box was opened. Inside were big golden oranges.

"Take your pick, Annie," said Mr. Odark.

Annie reached in and took out one of the oranges. On the orange was the same magic word that had been on the wooden box—CALIFORNIA.

She carried it outside into the cold. Annie held the orange close to her. She walked slowly behind the store and sat facing the bay. Then she closed her eyes and lifted the orange to her nose. CALIFORNIA. In her hands she held the wonder of the land she had learned about in school.

Little by little Annie took off the skin. She
placed the pieces carefully in her pocket. Later,
she could take the pieces of skin out and smell
them. Slowly she sank her teeth into the round
inside of the orange. Oh, it was so good. It was
like eating summer.

Soon the orange was half gone. Suddenly she
heard someone crying. She saw Emma coming
around the side of the store. Annie had never seen
anyone look so sad in her whole life.

When Emma saw Annie, she stopped crying.
Emma didn't want Annie to know how she really
felt.

"Emma," Annie said softly. "I didn't know you
were so sad."

Annie held out the half orange. "Here," she
said.

"What is it?" Emma took the orange and looked
at it carefully.

"It's an orange. I had one last year. Eat it."
Annie watched as Emma took a small bite.

"Isn't it good?"

Emma nodded.

This was the first thing that Annie had shared
with Emma without being told. Annie had a warm
feeling inside her.

"Please, you have some, too," Emma said. Her
voice was shy. She broke off a piece of the orange
and gave it to Annie.

Annie put the orange in her mouth, keeping her
teeth from it. She would have to remember this for
a whole year. This piece was the best of all. Annie
smiled. Emma didn't look sad anymore. Maybe
this was how it would be from now on, with Emma.

How Encyclopedia Brown Solved the Case of the Silver Fruit Bowl...

Chief Brown's words showed Encyclopedia where Mr. Herman had been lying.

Chief Brown said that the silver fruit bowl was rounded inside like a big spoon. Mr. Herman could not have had a good idea of what the holdup man looked like by looking into the fruit bowl, as he had said.

Look into a shiny spoon. What do you see? You see yourself as in a mirror, but **upside down!**

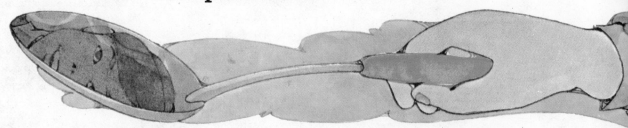

Faced with these facts, Mr. Herman told the real story. He had made up the story of the holdup man. He had stolen the silver dishes himself, hoping to sell them in another city and to keep all the money.

EXPLORING SPACE

You climb aboard a giant rocket. The countdown begins. 10, 9, 8, 7 . . . blast off! Suddenly you're headed for space, where the sky is always black and the stars are always shining.

Would you like to be an astronaut? An astronaut is *really* a sailor among the stars!

Astronaut Harrison Schmitt collects samples of the moon's surface.

Cosmonaut Valeriy Kubasov and Astronaut Thomas Stafford meet aboard Soyuz.

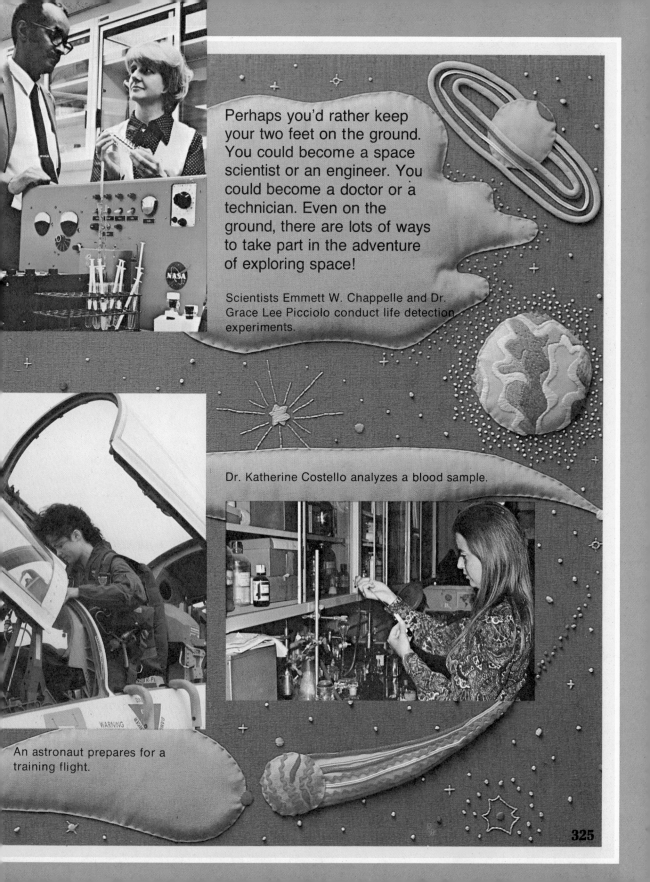

Perhaps you'd rather keep your two feet on the ground. You could become a space scientist or an engineer. You could become a doctor or a technician. Even on the ground, there are lots of ways to take part in the adventure of exploring space!

Scientists Emmett W. Chappelle and Dr. Grace Lee Picciolo conduct life detection experiments.

Dr. Katherine Costello analyzes a blood sample.

An astronaut prepares for a training flight.

Glossary

This glossary gives the pronunciations and meanings of some of the words used in this book.

The pronunciation is shown just after the word in this way: a•ble (ā′ bəl). The letters and signs are pronounced as shown in the words listed below.

If the word has more than one syllable, as in the example, a heavy accent mark ′ is placed after the syllable that receives the heaviest stress.

PRONUNCIATION KEY

a	hat	i	it	ou	out	w	will
ā	face	ī	ice	p	paper	y	yes
ä	father	j	jam	r	run	z	zoo
b	bad	k	kind	s	say	zh	treasure
ch	child	l	land	sh	she		
d	did	m	me	t	tell		
e	let	n	no	th	thin	ə stands for	
ē	be	ng	long	ŦH	then	a in about	
ėr	her	o	hot	u	cut	e in given	
f	fat	ō	open	ù	pull	i in family	
g	go	ô	or	ü	June	o in button	
h	he	oi	oil	v	very	u in walrus	

The pronunciation key, syllable breaks, and phonetic respellings in this glossary are adapted from the eighth edition of the *Thorndike-Barnhart Beginning Dictionary.* Users of previous editions or other dictionaries will find other symbols for some sounds.

FROM *THORNDIKE-BARNHART BEGINNING DICTIONARY* BY E. L. THORNDIKE AND CLARENCE L. BARNHART. COPYRIGHT © 1974 BY SCOTT, FORESMAN AND COMPANY. REPRINTED BY PERMISSION.

A

a·ble (ā′ bəl) having the power needed to do something

a·dult (ə dult′) full-grown

af·ford (ə fôrd′) to be able to pay for without hardship: *We can afford a new rug.*

A·las·kan (ə las′ kən) **1.** coming from or belonging to Alaska. **2.** someone born or living in Alaska

Al·ber·to (äl ber′ tō)

al·li·ga·tor (al′ ə gā′ tər) a large lizard with a long body, short legs, and strong jaws

a·lu·mi·num (ə lü′ mə nəm) **1.** a metal that is strong but light in weight. **2.** made of aluminum: *Mother bought aluminum pots.*

A·mer·i·ca (ə mer′ ə kə) **1.** The United States. **2.** North America and South America

A·mer·i·can (ə mer′ ə kən) **1.** coming from or belonging to America: *Apple pie is an American dish.* **2.** someone born or living in the United States

an·nu·al (an yü əl) once a year

art (ärt) **1.** the way or method of doing something. **2.** works, such as paintings, made by practicing an art

a·side (ə sīd′) away or set off to the side

at·tic (at′ ik) the part of a building just below the roof, sometimes used as a place to store things

auc·tion (ôk′ shən) a sale in which things are sold to the one who offers or bids the most money

au·di·ence (ôd′ ē əns) listeners; people who have gathered to watch and hear a show or music

B

band (band) people who play music together

bar·gain (bär′ gən) **1.** to be able to make a deal on price: *We had to bargain about the price.* **2.** a good buy

barge (bärj) a large, flat-bottomed boat used to carry goods

ba·ton (ba ton′) a stick or rod used by the director of a music group for beating time and leading the group

Be·del·ia (be dēl′ yə)

bee·tle (bē′ tl) an insect that has two hard, shiny cases that cover its wings when at rest

be·ware (bi wer′) be on your guard against; be careful

---

hat, fāce, fäther, let, bē, hėr, it, īce, hot, ōpen, ôr, oil, out, cut, pùll, Jüne, thin, ŦHen; ə stands for *a* in about, *e* in given, *i* in family, *o* in button, *u* in walrus.

bill·fold (bil′ fōld′) a folding purse for bills or paper money

block (blok) a four-cornered space in a town or city with a street on each side

board (bôrd) **1.** a piece of wood. **2.** a flat frame made for a special purpose: *Amy saw the sign on the bulletin board.* **3.** to be on a ship, plane, or train: *There were twenty people on board the ship.*

bow (bou) to bend from the waist

bow (bō) **1.** a tie made of ribbon or cloth. **2.** something used for shooting arrows. **3.** a rod strung with horse hair and used in playing the violin. See **violin.**

brain (brān) **1.** the mind or intelligence. **2.** someone who solves a mystery or is very bright: *Herman was the brain behind the plan.*

bridge (brij) **1.** something that carries a road over a body of water or land. **2.** the part of a violin that holds the strings up. See **violin.**

brin·dle cat (brin′ dl kat) a cat that is gray or tan with darker stripes

Bron·ti (bron′ tē)

Bron·to·saur·us (bron′ tə sôr′ əs)

bul·le·tin (bùl′ ə tən) **1.** a piece of news. **2.** having or carrying news: *The times for work are on the bulletin board.*

C

cal·i·co (kal′ ə kō) a cotton cloth, often having bright patterns

Cal·i·for·nia (kal′ ə fôr′ nyə) a state in the United States

car·di·nal (kärd′ n əl) an American songbird: *The male cardinal has bright red feathers marked with black.*

care·less·ly (ker′ lis lē) without any thought

Car·mel·a (kär mel′ ə)

Cher·o·kee (cher′ ə kē) **1.** the name of a tribe of North American Indians that once lived in Tennessee and North Carolina. **2.** a member of the Cherokee tribe. **3.** the language of the Cherokee people

chick·a·dee (chik′ ə dē′) a small bird with black, white, and gray feathers

chief (chēf) **1.** the head or leader. **2.** main; most important

Chi·na (chī′ nə) a country in Asia

chi·na-blue (chī′ nə blü) a gray-blue color

chore (chôr) everyday job: *Feeding the dog is an everyday chore.*

clar·i·net (klar′ ə net′) a wind instrument with a reed played by blowing through a mouthpiece and pressing keys

claw (klô) the sharp, hooked nail on the foot of an animal such as a bird or a cat

clerk (klėrk) someone who sells things in a store

com·ics (kom' iks) strips of pictures with words and balloons that tell stories

com·mon sense (kom' ən sens) good judgment in doing something or making a decision

con·trol (kən trōl') **1.** the power over something or someone. **2.** authority; direction. **3.** hold back; keep down

corn·meal (kôrn' mēl) corn ground into a powder used in making bread or cakes

crew (krü) the people who do the work on a ship or plane

crime (krīm) very wrong deed that is against the law

crunch (krunch) crush noisily with the teeth

crutch·es (kruch' əz) two supports made of wood or aluminum and used by lame people to help them walk

cus·tom (kus' təm) a way of acting that has been set up and kept going for a long time: *Indian tribes had customs that were different from the American settlers.*

D

dan·ger·ous (dān' jər əs) not safe; having the power to hurt or harm

deal (dēl) have to do with

den (den) **1.** the home of a wild animal, often a cave. **2.** hideaway

dent (dent) a hollow caused by a blow

de·tec·tive (di tek' tiv) someone who solves mysteries

dic·tion·ar·y (dik' shə ner' ē) a book that tells what words mean and how to say them

Di·Lu·ca (di lü' kə)

di·rec·tor (də rek' tər) someone who runs a business or tells people how to do things

dis·ap·pear (dis' ə pir') **1.** go away or out of sight. **2.** be used up

dis·ap·point (dis' ə point') make unhappy because something did not turn out as hoped for

dis·cov·er (dis kuv' ər) find out; see or learn for the first time

dis·may (dis mā') **1.** have a feeling of fear for what is about to happen or what has happened. **2.** trouble greatly; make afraid

---

hat, fāce, fäther, let, bē, hėr, it, īce, hot, ōpen, ôr, oil, out, cut, pull, Jüne, thin, ₮Hen; ə stands for *a* in about, *e* in given, *i* in family, *o* in button, *u* in walrus.

down·beat (doun′ bēt) down-swing of the hand or baton by the music director to show the players or singers the first beat of a piece of music

down·y wood·peck·er (dou′ nē wùd′ pek′ ər) one kind of bird that pecks holes in trees to get insects

drill (dril) to practice something over and over again

dun·geon (dun′ jən) a dark jail, usually underground

E

en·cy·clo·pe·di·a (en sī′klə pē′ dē ə) a book or set of books filled with facts in alphabetical order

en·gine (en′ jən) a machine that can make something move

Eng·land (ing′ glənd) an island country off the western shores of Europe

en·ve·lope (en′ və lōp) a paper cover in which a letter or anything flat can be mailed

ex·act·ly (eg zakt′ lē) in just the right way; correctly

F

fair (fer) just: *a fair decision*

fend·er (fen′ dər) the guard over the wheel of a car

Fi·del·ia (fi dēl′ yə)

fi·nal·ly (fī′ nəl ē) at the end; at last

finch (finch) a small songbird that is a seed eater

fire·crack·er (fīr′ krak′ ər) a small paper roll of gunpowder that makes a loud bang when lit

flour (flour) fine powder made of ground wheat and used in making bread and cake

frame (frām) a case that holds a picture or windowpane

fund (fund) money set aside for special use

G

gal·lop (gal′ əp) go very fast; hurry: *When a horse gallops, all four feet leave the ground with each leap.*

gar·lic (gär′ lik) a plant of the onion family, used to flavor foods

gasp (gasp) try hard to get one's breath through an open mouth: *A person gasps when out of breath or surprised.*

gen·er·al (jen′ ər əl) a leader of an army

gen·tle·man (jen′ tl mən) a man who is polite, kind, honest, and honorable

grace (grās) pleasing way of doing things or moving: *A good dancer must be graceful.*

grat·ing (grāt′ ing) crossed bars covering openings in sidewalks or streets

guard (gärd) watch over; to take care of; keep safe

H

ha·mal (hə mäl′) in some countries the name for someone whose job is to carry heavy things

hind (hīnd) at the back

hold·up (hōld′ up) a theft in which someone is made to hand over goods or money

hon·or (on′ ər) to think well of

hon·or·a·ble (on′ ər ə bəl) worthy of being well thought of

hun·ger (hung′ gər) the need for food

hut (hut) a small, poorly built house; cabin; shack

I

i·ci·cle (ī′ si kəl) pointed stick of ice that hangs down from a roof, window, or tree

in·stru·ment (in′ strə mənt) something that music may be played on

in·vis·i·ble (in viz′ ə bəl) not visible; out of sight

I·rish (ī′ rish) coming from or having to do with the country of Ireland

i·ron (ī′ ərn) a strong metal used in making pots and building materials; the metal from which steel is made

Ist·ven (ist′ vən)

J

Jap·a·nese (jap′ ə nēz′) coming from or having to do with the country of Japan

jeal·ous (jel′ əs) wanting something someone else has

jew·el (jü′ əl) a gem or stone worth much money

Jew·ish (jü′ ish) of Jewish people; belonging to Jewish people

Josh·u·a (josh′ ü ə)

June (jün) the sixth month

K

kid (kid) **1.** a child. **2.** a baby goat

king·dom (king′ dəm) a land ruled by a king or a queen

L

la·goon (lə gün′) a pond joined to a much larger body of water

lame (lām) unable to walk well because of a hurt or weak leg

lan·guage (lang′ gwij) written and spoken speech

lan·tern (lan′ tərn) case to protect a light from wind or rain

---

hat, fāce, fäther, let, bē, hėr, it, īce, hot, ōpen, ôr, oil, out, cut, pùll, Jüne, thin, ᴛнen; ə stands for *a* in about, *e* in given, *i* in family, *o* in button, *u* in walrus.

latch (lach) a catch or something to hold a door or gate closed

la·va (lä′ və) hot, melted rock flowing from a volcano

law (lô) a rule made by a country, state, or city

less (les) not so much as; a smaller amount: *The bag weighed less than two pounds.*

like·ly (līk′ lē) almost a sure thing: *Because of the storm, Allen is likely to be late.*

limp (limp) not stiff; very weak

Lyd·i·a (lid′ ē ə)

M

mag·net (mag′ nit) a piece of iron or steel that can draw to it other things made of iron or steel

man·age (man′ ij) to run; to control; to lead

Man·u·el (man wel′)

med·al (med′ l) a piece of metal like a coin given to honor a brave or good deed

Mex·i·ca·li (mek′ sə kal ē) from a city in Mexico

Mex·i·can (mek′ sə kən) **1.** belonging to or coming from Mexico. **2.** one who was born or who lives in Mexico

Mex·i·co (mek′ sə kō) the country just south of the United States

mist (mist) a cloud of damp air

Mount Ver·non (mount vėr′ nən) the home of George Washington

N

Na·than·iel (nə than′ yəl)

neigh·bor (nā′ bər) someone who lives next door or nearby

nut·hatch (nut′ hach′) a bird with a black cap and a long, sharp bill

O

O·dark (ô′ därk)

or·ches·tra (ôr′ kə strə) a group of people who play music on different instruments, including violins and string instruments as well as horns and other band instruments

or·der (ôr′ dər) **1.** a state of quiet, peace, or harmony. **2.** with *in,* to bring about: *We have to cross a bridge in order to get to the town.* **3.** the way things are arranged

or·phan (ôr′ fən) a child whose parents are dead

o·ver·board (ō′ vər bôrd′) from a ship or boat into the water: *The pole fell overboard.*

P

paint·ing (pān′ ting) picture made by using paints

pa·rade (pə rād') **1.** a march with or without music to show off a group of people, animals, or things. **2.** having to do with a parade: *First came the parade horses.*

pat·tern (pat' ərn) the way lines and colors are arranged

pegs (pegz) **1.** wooden nails. **2.** parts of a stringed instrument, used to tighten or loosen the strings. See **violin.**

pep·per (pep' ər) a red or green vegetable that may be used in soup or some other food

Per·i·an (per' ē ən)

pes·ter (pes' tər) to bother someone; to keep after

pitch (pich) a black, thick material taken from tar and used to cover roads

pleas·ure (plezh' ər) feeling of being pleased

pluck (pluk) pick or pull at; play a stringed instrument that way: *Sandy plucked the strings of the guitar.*

poor (pur) having few things or little money; lacking something

prac·ti·cal (prak' tə kəl) using good judgment; doing something that makes sense; useful

pres·i·dent (prez' ə dənt) the chief leader of a group, such as the people of a country

price·less (prīs' lis) very, very valuable

prick·le (prik'əl) tingle

proj·ect (proj' ekt) an undertaking; a plan

P.T.A. Parent-Teacher Association

pump (pump) **1.** something that may be used to lift or move air or water up into or out of something. **2.** to move air or water by means of a pump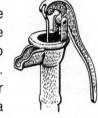

Q

queer (kwir) strange; odd

quill (kwil) a large stiff feather: *At one time people used a quill for a pen.*

quite (kwīt) **1.** fully; completely: *It is not quite dark.* **2.** really; truly: *There were quite a lot of people at the park.* **3.** somewhat; very: *I was sick, but I'm quite well, now.*

R

rack (rak) a frame with hangers for holding things

rage (rāj) violent anger

hat, fāce, fäther, let, bē, hėr, it, īce, hot, ōpen, ôr, oil, out, cut, pull, Jüne, thin, ᴛнen; ə stands for *a* in about, *e* in given, *i* in family, *o* in button, *u* in walrus.

rare (rar) not often seen or found

re·move (re müv′) get rid of

re·store (ri stôr′) to return; to put back or rebuild

row (rō) a line: *Stanley weeded the row of beans.*

ro·yal (roi′ əl) belonging to a king or queen

S

San·chez (san′ chez)

scalp (skalp) the skin on the top and back of the head

sci·ence (sī′ əns) **1.** the body of facts and laws that explain events; knowledge. **2.** a branch of learning, such as biology

Scor·i·a (skôr′ ē ə)

scout (skout) **1.** someone sent ahead to find things out or explore. **2.** a member of the Boy Scouts or Girl Scouts. **3.** having to do with or belonging to a scout

Se·at·tle (sē at′ əl) a seaport city in Washington State

sec·ond (sek′ ənd) **1.** coming after the first. **2.** one of the sixty small parts of time that make up a minute. **3.** a short span of time

Sei·go (sā′ gō)

se·quoi·a (si kwoi′ ə) a giant redwood tree of California

Se·quoy·ah (si kwoi′ ə) the great Indian who invented or made up a way of writing the Cherokee language and for whom the redwoods, or sequoias, are named

shag·gy (shag′ē) covered with or made of long thick hair; very hairy

sill (sil) the piece of wood at the bottom of a window or door

skip·per (skip′ ər) a captain of a ship

snatched (snacht) took quickly; grabbed

snout (snout) a long nose, especially of an animal such as a pig

sol·id (sol′id) hard; firm; strong

spin·ning wheel (spin′ ing hwēl) something for spinning flax or cotton into thread or yarn

stall (stôl) a place in a barn for a horse or a cow

starve (stärv) suffer very much because of hunger

state (stāt) part of a country: *The United States of America is made up of fifty states.*

Sta·vor·en (stä vôr′ ən)

steam (stēm) **1.** the gas made by boiling water. **2.** having steam. **3.** to use steam

steel (stēl) **1.** a strong product made from iron. **2.** made of steel

stick·ball (stik'bôl') a game like baseball, played with a stick instead of a bat

stuff (stuf) pack full; fill

stuff·ing (stuf' ing) filling

stump (stump) the part of the tree that is left after most of it has been cut off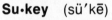

Su·key (sü'kē)

sul·tan (sult' n) in some countries, the ruler or king

sup·per (sup' ər) a light evening meal when dinner is eaten at noon

syl·la·bar·y (sil' ə ber' ē) a system of writing in which each letter stands for a syllable

syl·la·ble (sil' ə bəl) a word or part of a word spoken as a unit and made up of at least one vowel sound: *The word* spin *has one syllable. The word* spinning *has two syllables.*

T

tam·bou·rine (tam bə rēn') a small drum with metal disks played by striking it with the knuckles or by shaking it

tape (tāp) a thin strip of cloth, paper, or plastic with a sticky side used in wrapping packages and in making labels or name tags

tea·time (tē'tīm') a time for rest and something to eat and drink, usually in late afternoon

tel·e·scope (tel' ə skōp) an instrument that makes faraway things such as stars seem closer and bigger

thought·ful (thôt'fəl) **1.** full of thought; deep in thought. **2.** having the look of being deep in thought

trade (trād) **1.** the act of giving and getting things. **2.** to give something in exchange for something else

treas·ure (trezh' ər) something of great worth; valuable things: *The palace contains treasures.*

trom·bone (trom' bōn) a horn with a long sliding piece that is moved to make different sounds

---

hat, fāce, fäther, let, bē, hėr, it, īce, hot, ōpen, ôr, oil, out, cut, pùll, Jüne, thin, ᴛнen; ə stands for *a* in about, *e* in given, *i* in family, *o* in button, *u* in walrus.

trum·pet (trum′ pit)
a horn that is played
by blowing into a
mouthpiece and
pressing keys to
make sounds

trun·dle bed
(trun′ dəl bed) a
low bed that may be
stored under a big-
ger bed

U

un·like (un līk′) not like; different
from

use (yüz) **1.** to put to work. *Sue
said we could use her boat.* **2.** to
take or put in: *We use chicken to
make this soup.*

use (yüs) being put to work or
being used: *Jack made good use
of the cookbook.*

V

Val·ley Forge (val′ ē fôrj) a place
in Pennsylvania where George
Washington and his army spent
the winter of 1778

vin·tage (vin′ tij) having worth because of age

vi·o·lin (vī′ ə lin′) an
instrument with four
strings that is played
with a bow

vol·ca·no (vol kā′ nō) mountain
with an opening through which
steam, ashes, and lava sometimes
flow out

W

wal·rus (wôl′ rəs) a sea animal
that looks like a seal except for
its long tusks

wealth (welth) riches

weight (wāt) heaviness

west (west) **1.** the direction in
which the sun sets. **2.** the part of
a country that lies toward the west

whis·per (hwis′ pər) speak very
softly and low

wits (wits) one's mind; ability to
think: *She used her wits to find an
answer.*

Y

yo·gurt (yō′ gərt) a milk food